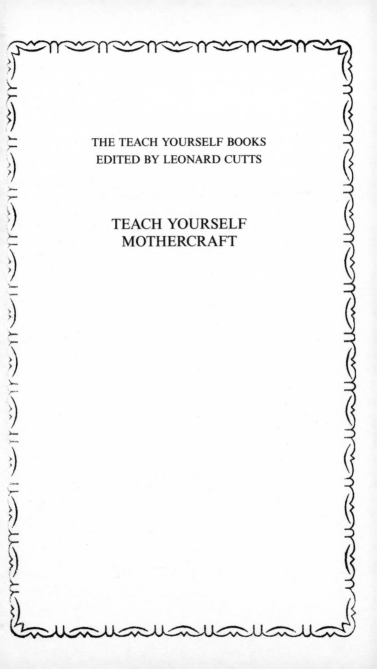

THE TEACH YOURSELF BOOKS
EDITED BY LEONARD CUTTS

TEACH YOURSELF
MOTHERCRAFT

In the same series

Teach Yourself Bird Watching
Teach Yourself Cycling
Teach Yourself Good Manners
Teach Yourself Motoring
Teach Yourself to Fly
Teach Yourself to Live

Teach®
Yourself

TEACH YOURSELF

MOTHERCRAFT

By
SISTER MARY MARTIN
S.R.N., S.C.M.

First published in Great Britain in 1950. Revised edition published in 1959.

This edition published in Great Britain in 2018 by John Murray Learning, an imprint of Hodder & Stoughton. An Hachette UK company.

British Library Cataloguing in Publication Data: a catalogue record for this title is available from the British Library.

Hardback: 978 1 473 68203 0
eBook: 978 1 473 68204 7

1

The publisher has used its best endeavours to ensure that any website addresses referred to in this book are correct and active at the time of going to press. However, the publisher and the author have no responsibility for the websites and can make no guarantee that a site will remain live or that the content will remain relevant, decent or appropriate.

The publisher has made every effort to mark as such all words which it believes to be trademarks. The publisher should also like to make it clear that the presence of a word in the book, whether marked or unmarked, in no way affects its legal status as a trademark.

Every reasonable effort has been made by the publisher to trace the copyright holders of material in this book. Any errors or omissions should be notified in writing to the publisher, who will endeavour to rectify the situation for any reprints and future editions.

Printed and bound in Great Britain by CPI Group (UK) Ltd., Croydon, CR0 4YY.

John Murray Learning policy is to use papers that are natural, renewable and recyclable products and made from wood grown in sustainable forests. The logging and manufacturing processes are expected to conform to the environmental regulations of the country of origin.

Carmelite House
50 Victoria Embankment
London EC4Y 0DZ
www.hodder.co.uk

FOREWORD

OUR children are more than our future. They are the most treasured possessions of our homes. My work as a Mothercraft Journalist, having brought me into close touch with many thousands of mothers—and of fathers too—has taught me to believe, as nothing else could have done, that the vast majority of present day parents are immensely keen to do their very best for their sons and daughters.

Throughout their pregnancies, and again during the tender years of life when the relationships between parent and child are so closely woven, most mothers seek eagerly both guidance and help. In " Teach Yourself Mothercraft," I have endeavoured to give that help in a simple, straightforward way.

The instinct of motherhood is very strong in woman and although good mothers, it is true, are born rather than made, it is, surely, when instinct is wedded to knowledge that a real craft emerges.

And, as a pinnacle rising above all others, does not mothercraft stand supreme ?

MARY MARTIN.

CONTENTS

INDEX TO CHARTS

ILLUSTRATIONS

A*

Being a parent carries with it big responsibilities and brings great compensations.

CHAPTER I

HAPPY HOMES

A HAPPY baby means a happy mother. A happy mother makes a happy home.

There must be exceptions to this rule, of course, as there are to any other, but I believe those exceptions are so few, and so far between, that we can safely ignore them and accept the thought as it stands. Happy babies and happy mothers are two of the chief ingredients that go to make up happy homes.

The first step towards possessing a bonny, happy baby yourself, is study and to understand the simple essentials of mothercraft. It is a great joy to be able to watch your little one with real pride and see him grow sturdier every day under your loving care; to know that his firm flesh, his steady gains, his easy tooth cutting, his happy nature—in short, his fine constitution and un-bounding good health—are a direct result of your own efforts and the outcome of knowledge sensibly applied.

The second step, which is just as important as the first, is to appreciate that while there is a right and a wrong way of doing things for a baby, no two children are exactly alike; what suits one, may not always suit another. Even in the same family, this can be very apparent and so you must not be surprised if, for instance, your second child behaves in a way very different from your first.

And the third step, no less vital than the other two, is to realise that your own age, within reason, is probably not nearly so important to mothercraft as your mental attitude towards motherhood and child bearing, especially now when such big advances have been made and so

Children ask for love, not riches.

much is being done to ensure the well-being, the comfort and the health of every mother and of every child.

Having a baby is the supreme fulfilment of your own biological and physiological function. It is a natural and a normal happening and it is one that you should be able to anticipate with interest and with joy.

It is true that being a parent carries with it big responsibilities, but it brings also great compensations, and no home can be said to be truly complete whose walls have never echoed with the merry sound of childish laughter.

Children do not ask for riches ; worldly goods mean nothing to them. Their primary needs in early life apart from food and clothing, are to be loved, to be conscious of being wanted, to feel secure, and to be allowed to share those things, however simple and however humble, that their fathers and their mothers are able to provide.

Baby's Birthright

The very first paving stones to good health are laid down while a baby is still developing within his mother's womb. That is one reason why those nine prenatal months are so very important.

The more fully you appreciate this fact, the better you will be able to realise just what a big part you are destined to play in giving each one of your children the good health that ought to be theirs.

If you follow reliable and up to date antenatal (before birth) advice, and understand what you are doing and why you are doing it, events should go along very smoothly. What is more, as you watch your little ones grow, you will know in your heart that you have done everything in your power to give them the fine start in life that is every baby's birthright.

Mothercraft

Children should be a joy, never a burden. Provided

they are properly managed they are, by nature, happy little people. Make a few bad mistakes, though, and instead of a gurgling, contented infant, or a joyous, carefree child, we may find a very different picture. And, I know from experience, that nothing upsets a mother sooner than to find that all is not well with her baby. It may be that he is not gaining as fast as he

A father's influence cannot be over-estimated.

should be ; or that he has indigestion, or wind ; or that he is hungry. He may wake up crying in the night, not just once, but two or three times and on several nights in succession. If his mother does not know what is wrong or how to put things right, it will not be long before worn out through broken rest and lack of proper sleep, her own nerves, and possibly those of her husband also will begin to fray under the strain.

By learning all you can about mothercraft now and putting your knowledge to good use, you will be able to avert troubles of this kind.

Parentcraft

Both mother and father are immensely important people in the eyes of a baby, and while it is of necessity his mother who takes the greatest share in looking after him and caring for him while he is tiny, mothercraft is not without its complement, fathercraft.

The influence of a father on his children and on his home, cannot be over-estimated. When both parents share the difficulties and the responsibilities, as well as the interests and the joys of their family, we have a combination which leaves a very deep and lasting impression in the minds of the children.

Fathercraft

As soon as your husband finds himself in the position of being a prospective father, do let him take his full and rightful share in parenthood with you.

There are so many things he can do, and will take a pride in doing ; so many ways he can help you along. While you are carrying he should realise that far from being an invalid you ought to be, and you probably are, better in health than ever before. Because of this, you may try to overdo things sometimes. It is then that he ought to be ready to curb your activities, gently always, but effectively nevertheless.

During the early months of pregnancy when you may be feeling sick, he can bring you a cup of tea in bed in the morning. He can lay and light the fires, carry in coal for the day, be firm about your leaving the heavier household jobs for him to do when he gets home in the evening. If you seem tired, he can bring your supper to you in bed.

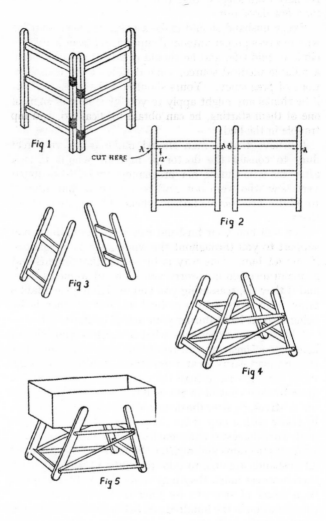

Fig 1

CUT HERE   12"

Fig 2

Fig 3

Fig 4

Fig 5

He may even suggest that you go away to some relative for a few days' rest.

Every husband should make a point of seeing that his wife receives proper antenatal supervision from a doctor, clinic or midwife, and he should obtain for himself from a reliable medical source, some details of the complications of pregnancy. Yours should do the same. Then, if he thinks any might apply to you, or if he sees signs of one of them starting, he can obtain medical aid, and nip trouble in the bud.

I believe that a man should make it his very real duty to consult the doctor or midwife who is to look after his wife during her pregnancy, and I have found very few who were not glad to interview and anxious to advise prospective fathers whenever they went to see them.

You will find your husband can be a wonderful moral support to you throughout the whole of your pregnancy if you let him. One way is by seeing that friends and acquaintances do not worry you with old women's tales, and if they do, reassuring you and explaining such fables away from a sensible, practical angle. Another is by being near at hand during your actual confinement.

I know from experience what a comfort and what a help a good husband can be at this time. I know, too, that no man earns greater gratitude from his wife when she is having a baby than the one who can be depended upon to take control in the home, see to callers, inform the relatives, go after the doctor or midwife, boil up water, be ready with a cup of tea, have a set of tools handy to deal with domestic emergencies like broken fuse wires, send off telegrams and register the birth. Of course, not all husbands are able to take the time off to be at home then however much they may wish to, but they can still be a tower of strength by their forethought and their consideration in the hundred and one ways that are bound to present themselves.

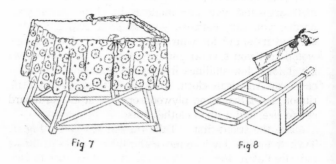

Fig 7   Fig 8

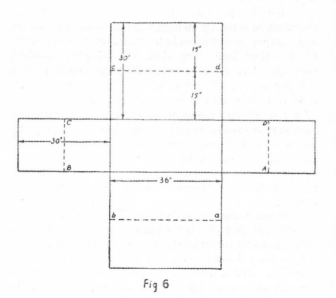

Fig 6

Things You Can Make

If your husband is handy with a hammer—and most men are—and you are moderately clever with your needle, you can, between you, make a charming little cot and its stand for your baby (Fig. 7). To buy, this would cost you several guineas, but you will be able to get it for a few shillings from some 36-inch wide strong calico or American cloth, some pretty material, a little ribbon, six laths, some plywood or very stout cardboard cut to size, and a small clothes horse.

Make the stand first. Take the clothes horse, Fig. 1. Turn it upside down, remove the hinges and cut off as indicated at A, Fig. 2. Place the two pieces face to face as in Fig. 3, and securely nail or screw three laths to each side, Fig. 4. Rub the stand over with fine glass-paper and give two or three coats of good paint.

To make the cot, Fig. 5, mark out one strip of material, the width of stand by 96 inches (2 yards, 24 inches) long, and another 36 inches wide by 60 inches *plus* the width of the stand long. Cut these out allowing half-inch turnings. Lay these crosswise over one another as in the diagram (Fig. 6) and securely stitch the sides A to a, B to b, C to c, and D to d. Fold over at the dotted lines and slip two pieces of plywood or thick cardboard each approximately 36 inches long by 15 inches high up between the two folds forming each of the sides of the cot, and two others 15 inches high and as wide as the cot stand up between the two folds forming the top and bottom. Oversew the open edges where these went in.

Then cut a piece of plywood to form a firm base for the cot and over this lay a piece of material and catch stitch down all round to the bottom of the cot.

Line the cot inside with any material you fancy and drape the outside with a 16-inch deep frill of muslin or organdi, making a little coverlet of the same material. Arrange a piece of material gathered at both ends at the head to ward off draughts and add a finish, and finally trim with ribbon rosettes or bows, Fig. 7.

A nursing chair is a blessing in any house where there is a baby. Perhaps your husband will be able to make one for you himself. If not, he can, with very little trouble, convert any comfortable light chair into a nursing chair by sawing a few inches off its four legs leaving the two back ones two inches shorter than the two front, so that it tilts the seat slightly backwards.

Bringing up Baby

Bringing up a baby is really a joint concern, and although every mother and every father, too, should know that from the day their child is born his character will begin to mould itself and take shape as he grows, the environment surrounding the home into which he comes is going to make its mark well and truly on the subconscious of his mind from the very start.

That is why the early years of infancy are so important. That is why, ideally, a baby should find himself in happy surroundings, with loving parents and amongst balanced emotions. It is good for a child—even quite a tiny one— to find that his father and his mother love each other deeply, and yet at the same time, have plenty of love to shower on him.

It is equally good for him to find that he is one of the cogs that go to make up the home wheel ; not the only cog or, even worse, the wheel itself. One of the first things children have to learn is that they must revolve with everybody else round the home circle ; not expect the home to begin to revolve round them.

Right from the early days both mother and father should agree on points concerning their children when within their hearing. Mother's word must be the same as father's—always. If your husband has forbidden some particular thing, you must do the same, otherwise you will cause confusion in your child's mind. Even if you feel your husband is wrong, uphold him, and in the same way he should uphold you.

At the same time, if either of you have made a mistake or committed some error of judgment and the child is old enough to realise this, it is best to admit it quite

Little will escape the scrutiny of his eye.

frankly.   After all, you would expect your child to own up if the circumstances were reversed.

In this and in many other ways as soon as you are a parent, you will have to exercise a care that might never have been necessary before.   You will have to be constantly on the watch.   Because children model themselves on their elders' behaviour, your baby will copy you and your husband, and model his thoughts, words and actions on what you say and do. You may not think so but little indeed will escape the scrutiny of his critical eye, his sharp ear and impressionable brain.

You must never forget for a moment that right from the day baby is born you will be sowing the seeds of his character, and what you sow when he is tiny he will reap when he is older. Make sure, then, that what you sow, you sow well and you sow wisely. Only the best and the highest is good enough for the little one that is to be your child and your husband's.

CHAPTER II

THE EXPECTANT MOTHER

DURING his mother's carrying months, the little child has to develop from one single cell, almost too small to be seen with the naked eye, to a perfect human person. This takes roughly two hundred and eighty days.

Reckoning Up

There is more than one method of reckoning up to find out when a baby will be born, but the best I think, and certainly the simplest, is to count forward seven days from the first day of the last normal period and then add on to that nine calendar months.

If you adopt this method too, you cannot go far wrong. At the same time, we have to remember that very few babies are absolutely punctual ; some are born a few days before their appointed date ; some a few days after it.

Let us take an example so that you can see how it works out. Suppose the last normal period started on June 1st. By adding on seven days we arrive at June 8th, and by counting forward nine calendar months from June 8th it brings us to March 8th, which is the approximate date of the birth. There are obstetric tables which take into account the irregular number of days in the various months, but tables are by no means essential outside professional hands, and even many doctors dispense with them and reckon up by the method I have given or one similar to it.

Early Signs

The usual early signs of pregnancy are a missed period,

Visit your doctor early in pregnancy.

tenderness and possibly enlargement of the breasts, sickness in the early morning (or nausea) and a desire to pass water more frequently than before. Some expectant mothers experience a certain amount of backache but by no means all, and quite a few are not sick and do not even feel sick. While there are a few who may see a slight period during the first and second months, it cannot be regarded as completely normal. In fact, it may indicate a threat to miscarry. Nearly all pregnant women, though, notice the discomfort in the breasts to a greater or lesser degree, while as time goes on the skin round the nipple tends to become a dark brown in brunettes, and to turn a deeper pink in the fair-skinned mothers.

Visiting the Doctor

As soon as possible after missing your first period, or if you have reason to think that you are pregnant before that, you should visit your doctor or midwife for the first time, or attend at a welfare or an antenatal clinic.

Some doctors and some midwives, too, like to make an internal examination at this visit but most prefer to wait till later. What they all will do, though, is to ask you a few general questions regarding your health, your age, the number of years you have been married, the date of your last period and, if this is not your first baby, they will want to know something about your previous confinements. So tell them all you know as frankly as you can. Try and be concise. If some of the details seem intimate to you, never mind. Doctors and nurses always understand.

Yours will probably test your urine and take your blood pressure, and look at your breasts and nipples. They will discuss with you where to have baby, in a hospital, in your own home or a nursing or maternity home.

After your first antenatal visit you should continue to attend the doctor or midwife at regular intervals, not because there is anything wrong, but to make sure that everything is right and remains right. During the last eight weeks of pregnancy the visits are usually increased from once a month to once a fortnight.

Each time you go, take with you a sample of your urine that has been passed first thing in the morning. Pour it into a clean bottle, labelled with your name, the date and the words " specimen of urine." This specimen should be free from vaginal secretions because it will have to be chemically tested, so wash yourself carefully before you pass it and use a perfectly clean receptacle to collect it in.

Visiting the Dentist

The condition of your teeth is very important both to you and to baby. Not only are his first set of teeth beginning to form before birth, but so are his second or permanent ones. The quality of his teeth will depend largely on your health and diet during pregnancy. Bad teeth are bad for you and therefore bad for baby. So, you should visit your dentist twice, or better still, three times during your carrying months.

Make the first visit to him when you are about three months on the way, the second when you are in your fifth month, and then one more when you enter the eighth month. If the dentist finds a small cavity it will give him a chance to stop it and in this way your teeth will be preserved and the chance of extractions prevented.

At the same time, if it should be necessary to have a tooth out, there should be nothing to fear. But to leave a decayed tooth unattended to is dangerous. It harbours germs, and every time you swallow, poisons from those germs are swallowed too. That is very bad for you and for your baby because the germs get into the blood and circulate round the body. Always look on decaying teeth therefore as harmful. Have them stopped when they need it, and if they are too bad for this be guided by your dentist and have them out, but do have artificial ones

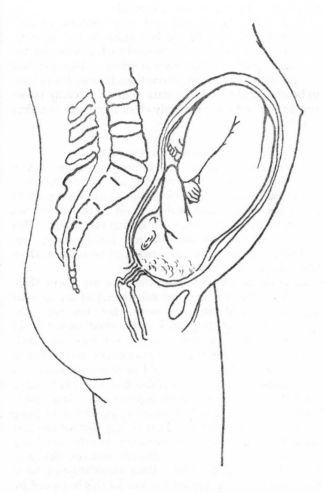

How your baby lies before birth.

to fill the gaps. It is important that you masticate your food properly and you cannot do this if some teeth are missing.

Work of the Body

During the whole of your pregnancy your body is working for two people. It is nourishing you and getting rid of your waste, and it is nourishing your baby and getting rid of his waste.

It stands to reason, therefore, that the healthier and the better equipped you keep your body, the healthier and the bonnier your baby should be.

The baby in the womb needs very liberal supplies of body-building material. The question you and every expectant mother must ask herself is this : Where does my baby get all these materials from ? The answer is: From the food his mother eats.

After digestion the mother's food passes into her blood stream. From her blood her baby extracts whatever he needs for his own use. In exchange for what he takes, he gives up (into his mother's blood) impurities from his own growing body, and then it becomes the task of the mother's kidneys to excrete both her baby's waste and much of her own through the medium of her urine.

You will now realise why it is so important to try and keep your blood stream well stocked with everything your own developing baby is going to need, and why at the same time, it must stay as pure as possible—that is, free from too much of your own waste. If it is not then your kidneys may find themselves with more work than they can comfortably cope with, and as a result your own health and baby's, too, will be very liable to suffer.

CHART 1
TWO SPECIMEN MENUS FOR THE EXPECTANT MOTHER

BREAKFAST: Fruit salad sprinkled with raw oatmeal. Egg or bacon dish. Toast and butter with honey. Weak tea or coffee.

DINNER: Milk soup. Fish or chop. Green or root vegetables, potatoes. Stewed fruit. Water to drink.

TEA: Grated cheese sandwiches. Plain or fruit cake. Weak tea.

SUPPER: Fish or egg dish. Green salad*. Junket. Orange juice or milk to drink.

BREAKFAST: Fresh fruit or baked apple. Kipper or grilled herring. Toast and marmalade with butter. Weak coffee.

DINNER: Roast mutton, rabbit or baked liver. Roast potatoes. Greens. Stewed fruit and custard. Water or orange juice and water to drink.

TEA: Fruit salad†. Egg sandwiches. Weak tea.

SUPPER: Lentil cutlets, or fish or cheese dish with vegetables. Fresh or dried fruit. Milk to drink.

Each day: The juice of at least one whole orange or its equivalent well diluted, and some cod- or halibut-liver oil or their equivalent in vitamin capsules or tablets.

* GREEN SALAD: Shred finely one raw cabbage leaf, half a raw carrot, 3 dandelion leaves. Add a round of beetroot, a sprig of parsley and any two of the following, chopped finely: Onion, mint, lettuce, cauliflower, sprouts, turnip tops, kale or watercress. Garnish with cold diced potato. The potato can be cooked. All other ingredients should be raw.

† FRUIT SALAD: Stew 1 apple or 3 apple rings, 2 prunes, 6 sultanas. To these, add any fresh fruit in season or any dried, tinned or bottled fruit you have, and pour two teaspoons of orange juice or some rose-hip syrup over the salad.

Diet During Pregnancy

Diet during pregnancy is immensely important. Firstly because, as we have seen, the baby needs the right materials to build bones, flesh, muscle, fat and blood, secondly because pregnancy always throws a certain amount of additional work on to the mother's kidneys.

The ideal food is extra rich in body-building materials for the baby's sake, and particularly free from anything that will increase the work of the eliminating organs (chiefly the kidneys) for the mother's sake.

Your diet should be light and easily digested. Heavy boiled puddings, rich and twice cooked dishes, pastries, food consisting chiefly of starch like rice, tapioca and white bread should be avoided. The best foods for you now are meat, liver, fish, chicken, rabbit, cheese, eggs, peas, beans and lentils all of which contain good body-building elements. In addition you need milk, vegetables of all kinds, vegetarian dishes, green and other uncooked vegetables, salads, all fruits (fresh, dried, bottled or canned), nuts (if well chewed and eaten with meals), junket, milk puddings and custard, milk jellies, milk soups, cereals, brown toast, wholemeal bread, home-made cakes, honey, syrup, jams and marmalade, chocolate and all forms of vegetable extracts.

Milk is a highly valuable food and at the very least you should take a full pint every day. Other good fluids include cocoa, barley water and any and all kinds of fruit juices and water. Tea and coffee can be taken but both should be weak and the former freshly made. Aim at drinking four pints of fluid each day, and supplement the ordinary vitamins found in diet with some additional ones.

The additional vitamins you need are Vitamins A, C and D. Orange juice, rose-hip syrup and black currants are very rich in Vitamin C. Cod and halibut liver oils or else vitamin tablets will give you Vitamins A and D.

Clothes During Pregnancy

Comfort, neatness, economy and good service should be the keynote of your maternity wear. But this need not mean a large outlay either in money or in garments. Many of your existing ones can probably be altered and adapted quite easily, so leaving you very little to buy.

During the early months most expectant mothers wear their usual clothes, and only get maternity wear for the latter part of their pregnancies. The following list gives you a complete maternity outfit, but as those items marked * are probably already in your wardrobe, in one form or another, it leaves very few things to get.

```
1 mackintosh* for wet days
1 dress for maternity wear
1 skirt for maternity wear
2 loosely fitting jumpers* (or 1 smock and 1 jumper*)
1 coatee* (or jersey*) for chilly days
2 pairs of comfortable shoes*
3 vests*
2 or 3 pairs of knickers*  ⎫
2 or 3 petticoats*          ⎬ or 2 or 3 camiknickers*
1 maternity belt           ⎭
2 uplifting brassières
2 or 3 nightdresses* (or pairs of pyjamas*)
1 dressing gown*
1 pair of bedroom slippers*
```

So far as can be arranged, garments should hang from the shoulders now, particularly skirts. This is easily possible if you make two rather wide shoulder straps, work a buttonhole at both ends of each strap (Fig. 13) and then to the skirt waistband, sew four buttons to button the straps to back and front, rather like braces.

Petticoats, knickers and nightdresses should be on the large size, especially round the waist. If you adapt your petticoats and nightdresses so that they have front or shoulder openings, they can be used throughout the nursing period without further alterations.

You can wear your usual corset or roll-ons for the first three or four months, but as your figure enlarges it is best to discard these for a maternity belt.

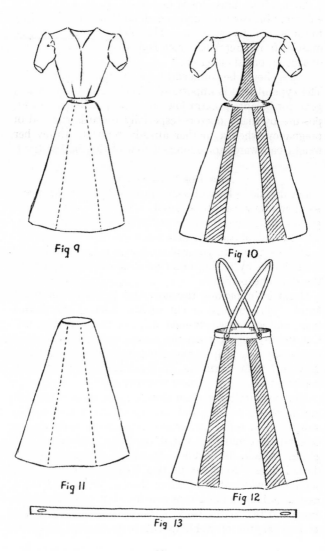

Fig 9

Fig 10

Fig 11

Fig 12

Fig 13

An uplifting brassière is essential. It should cup the enlarging breasts from underneath and draw them slightly towards the breast bone. This helps to prevent the muscles from stretching which is, perhaps, the main cause of sagging breasts later on.

Shoes should be comfortable and they should be light. The type of heel is important. Very high heels are not good for balance ; extra low ones are considered bad for posture by many doctors, especially towards the end of pregnancy when a mother already tends to throw her weight backwards to counteract that of the child in front.

Altering Your Clothes

Let us take a look at some quite ordinary clothes and see how they can be altered. Dresses, skirts, night-gowns, petticoats, knickers and brassières all lend themselves to adaptation for maternity wear quite easily.

In Figs. 9 and 10 you will see how a plain dress can be made larger by letting in strips of contrasting colour to the skirt and bodice.

Begin by unpicking the skirt and top from the waist band. Then unpick or cut up the skirt at the dotted lines, and let in two six-inch strips of material (Fig. 10). Cut the bodice right up the centre front and let in an eight-inch wide strip of material here. Hem the top and draw up with a ribbon draw-string. Then set both bodice and skirt into a new waistband.

Now for altering a plain skirt. Figs. 11 and 12 show you how this is done and how to attach it to shoulder straps. You begin by removing the waist band on the original skirt and then cut it right up the front in two places (A and B in Fig. 11) where indicated by the dotted lines. Next let in two V-shaped pieces which should be wider at the bottom than at the top, attach a new waistband and on to it sew four buttons, two at the front and two at the back. The shoulder straps consist of two lengths of webbing cut to your own measurements (each about 32 inches long) with button holes at both ends to take the buttons on the waistband. (Fig. 13).

In Fig. 14, you will see how simple it is to alter an

Fig 14

Fig 15

ordinary nightdress by inserting strips of similar or of contrasting material and arranging for button and button-hole opening where indicated. These are for use during breast feeding after baby is born.

In the petticoat (Fig. 15) the shoulder straps have been altered so that they now button to the front of the petticoat top. This is to facilitate breast feeding later on, while the widening material has been inserted up the whole length of the side seams on both sides.

Two methods of enlarging a pair of knickers are given in Figs. 16 and 17. One (Fig. 16) shows a sideseam widening, the other (Fig. 17) not so easy to do, has the

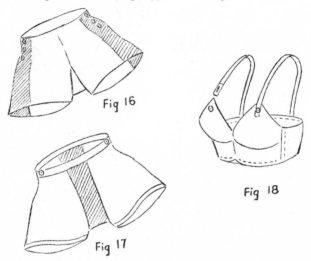

Fig 16

Fig 18

Fig 17

widening at the front and back seams. New waist bands will be needed in each case.

Fig. 18 illustrates an ordinary brassière and shows you how to convert it into a nursing one. All you have to do is to unpick each shoulder strap in front, neaten the ends and then sew on a loop to form a button hole. To the brassière itself you sew two buttons in their appropriate places.

Figs. 19 and 20 give two extremely simple ways of adapting a skirt, dress and coat to maternity wear. The side seams of the skirt are merely unpicked for a distance of six or eight inches below the waist level, the two openings are hemmed and tapes are attached for tying.   Over this skirt you wear a smart smock.   After baby is born all you need to do is to remove the tapes, sew up the seams once more, and the skirt can be put back into ordinary use once again.

Fig 19

Fig 20

A dress can be similarly adapted. Both side seams are unpicked for a few inches above as well as below the waist level and tapes for fastening are attached.   Instead of wearing a smock, a light edge to edge coat (Fig 20) is worn over this dress to conceal the openings and give the appearance of a coat frock.

Your Maternity Belt

Maternity belts take the place of the usual suspender belt, roll-ons or corsets. These can be bought ready-made or you can make an excellent belt at home for very little money, and if you look at Fig. 21 you will see a simple, yet effective one illustrated there.   For this, you

will need approximately a yard-and-a-half of strong
material about twelve inches wide. To make the belt,
first hem the two long edges making the lower hem much
deeper than the upper one. Then hem each of the two
short ends. You now have a long narrow strip of material
hemmed all round with a good, firm, lower edge. (Fig. 22).

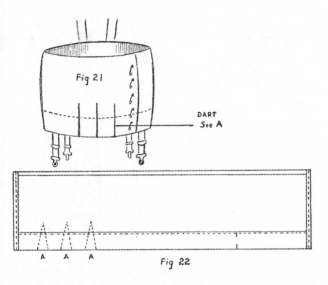

Fig 21

DART
See A

Fig 22

At the bottom edge (the one with the deep hem) and
eight inches from one end, make a large dart measuring
about one inch wide at the bottom tapering off to nothing
six inches up. This dart forms the centre front of your
belt. Four inches on either side of it make two other
similar darts. (As pregnancy advances these darts can
be readjusted to fit the altering figure.) To the lower
edge of the belt, clip or sew on two pairs of suspenders,
and to the top edge, at the centre back, attach two wide
webbing straps. These come over the shoulders like
braces, and fasten with safety pins to the belt in front.

To put on the maternity belt, lie down on your bed with the belt in position under you. Make sure that its lower edge is at least eight inches below the waist-line, and then wrap it round the abdomen, turn in any surplus and fasten down one side with large, strong safety pins. Next, adjust the shoulder straps and suspenders. The belt should fit tightly round the hips, but be comparatively loose at and above the waist level. Its object is to lift and support the abdomen ; not to compress it.

Exercise

Every expectant mother needs adequate exercise and it is very important that she should get it. So try and take two brisk walks every day. If you are not accustomed to going far, start by going a short distance only and gradually increase it. You must dress to suit the weather, and never allow a wet day to keep you in unless, of course, the rain is particularly severe. Towards the end of your pregnancy, you may have to curtail your walks somewhat, but a certain amount of time should be spent out of doors all the same, weather permitting.

If you are a cyclist it is advisable to obtain your doctor's opinion as to whether or not you may continue to ride now. Some allow an expectant mother to bicycle ; others quite forbid it. The same applies to games and sports in general, but all doctors agree that the daily walk is of the utmost benefit to a normally healthy woman, and most permit sea bathing provided the water is calm.

When you are indoors make a point of getting all the fresh air you possibly can. Never sit for long in a room where the windows are closed, and since the night air is particularly pure, make a point of opening your window before getting into bed.

In addition, with your doctor's permission you can do a few set exercises each day and Chart 2 illustrates and describes three good ones.

CHART 2
EXERCISES FOR THE EXPECTANT MOTHER

Lie flat in a comfortable position. Stretch every limb and muscle to its fullest extent then quickly go to the other extreme—completely limp. Yawn and imagine your body becoming a dead, dead weight. Continue with this line of thought giving up all tension in turn in the feet, legs, abdomen, hands, arms, neck and lastly the face and head. Try to dismiss all but happy and restful thought from your mind and remain relaxed as a prelude to sleep.

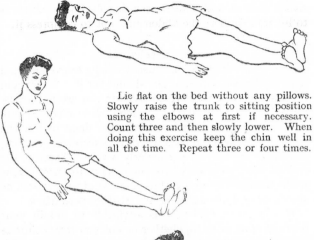

Lie flat on the bed without any pillows. Slowly raise the trunk to sitting position using the elbows at first if necessary. Count three and then slowly lower. When doing this exercise keep the chin well in all the time. Repeat three or four times.

Grasp the back of a firm chair. Keep the heels together. Raise up on to the toes and lower slowly to squatting position (sitting on the heels). The knees should be well apart. Return to the starting position and repeat the exercise six times, keeping the back hollowed and rounded alternately as you lower on to your heels.

The first exercise should be done when commencing your afternoon rest, and again last thing at night ; the other two when your are fresh in the morning.

39

Rest

While it is true that you need regulated exercise now, you also need sufficient rest. If you can arrange for an hour on your bed in the afternoon, or if you go out to work, then on your arrival home, you will find it a big help. If not, try and sit with your feet up and really relax for a few moments whenever you do get a chance.

In any case, aim at getting a full eight hours in bed each night in a cool, well-ventilated room. Tuck a small pillow under the abdomen to support it while you are lying on your side, and place it in the hollow of your spine if you lie on your back. If you experience difficulty in sleeping, or find it hard to drop off at night, try adding an extra pillow to raise the head higher, breathe deeply and slowly and practise your relaxation exercise.

A wakeful night now and again need not trouble you at all. Just relax, occupy your mind with cheerful thoughts, and remember that the quiet rest in the dark is doing you and baby good even though you may not actually be asleep.

Old Wives' Tales

No sensible mother takes the slightest notice of old wives' tales in these days. She realises that it is quite harmless to sit with her legs crossed ; to play with kittens and puppies ; to be startled by a mouse ; to satisfy or deny ordinary cravings ; to cover her face with her hands or sleep with her arms above her head. She realises, too, that a sick pregnancy does not mean an easy birth or vice versa, and she knows that carrying to the front does not mean the birth of a son. She knows, also, that a change in health does not forecast a change of birth, or a change of sex.

All these sayings are just idle chatter, and if anyone comes to you with some old wives' tale the wisest thing to do is to smile, and ignore it. You know that baby is perfectly safe and that he could not possibly be marked because of something you did, for instance, or something you saw, or because of anything you thought of, or heard about. When I tell you that the number of perfect babies born every week runs into thousands ; and the numbers with some tiny fault so few, that there is no need to count them, you will know that you need not worry.

Where both parents are healthy and well the chances are hundreds to one that their baby will be the same.

Birthmarks

Birthmarks are never caused by having intercourse near to the commencement of a period or at the end of it, or even during the menstrual flow. They are usually due to dilated blood vessels in the surface of the skin, or possibly to some unusual pressure before or during birth. In these days birthmarks are generally removable in the few cases where they do not fade naturally during the first year or so of life.

In the same way, slight deformities are not due to a mother suffering some fright, or to her covering her eyes with her hands if she is startled, or any similar notion of this kind. They result from a small developmental error, or some very unusual state of health on the part of one of the parents, or some other purely medical reason. They, too, are so rare that you can ignore them, completely.

All the same, if you are feeling secretly worried about something you have heard or may have thought you have read, by far the best thing to do is to tell your doctor or nurse all about it. They will understand, and their word may always be taken as absolute fact. Remember, though, the brighter and happier you are and the more sensible your own outlook is on life, the better it will be for your baby. The reason for this is simple, People who are cheerful nearly always enjoy better health than those who are downcast.

The better your own health, therefore, the better

chance you will have of passing good health on to your child.   It is a fact worth remembering.

Quickening

When you are between sixteen and twenty weeks pregnant, you will feel baby move for the first time. This is called " the quickening " and when it happens a mother is said to have " quickened." You must not imagine that the first movement you feel will necessarily be the first movement your baby makes. Probably it will not.

Most babies have been moving for quite a few days before their mothers recognise the slight fluttering sensations going on inside them to be the actual movements made by their unborn child. But look out for this quickening as you approach the time for it, and make a note of the date, because your doctor may ask you if you have quickened yet, and if so, when.

The quickening is a normal and natural happening. It is quite unaccompanied by any unpleasant sensations or emotions on the part of the mother, so do not expect any violent or alarming symptoms. What you will and should experience, though, is a renewed joyful anticipation of motherhood and the knowledge that as time goes on, your baby's movements will become very much stronger, and much more frequent.

Preparation of the Breasts

There is no food quite so good for the human baby as human milk, and during the nine months that you are carrying your child, your breasts are getting ready to provide the milk that he will need after his birth.   Here, three things are going to help a lot.   They are :

1.   Good nipples
2.   Free channels for the milk to flow through
3.   Efficient functioning of the milk glands.

Any time and effort you spend helping your breasts to

get ready for this task may show little for your trouble during your waiting period, but once baby has arrived you should be repaid a thousand times.

If your nipples do not stand out well, or if they are depressed or inverted, doctors now recommend their expectant mother patients to wear nipple shells over the nipple area and under the brassière during the day-time from quite early in pregnancy.

These shells cause no inconvenience to the wearer but the effect they have on the nipples is almost miraculous. By exerting a gentle and continuous pressure they coax each nipple outwards, and by the time the baby is born the result should be two well-formed nipples.

The human nipple is rather like the rose on the end of a garden watering can. The surface of each nipple is pierced by about sixteen to twenty minute holes. These are the openings of the little milk ducts which connect with the interior of the breast.

Not infrequently some of these are blocked at the start; others are very small. That we have found is one reason why some mothers have trouble with their breasts. The milk cannot flow freely through all the little channels when the baby sucks. Some of it gets held back and, as a result, the breasts themselves quickly become uncomfortable, hard and over-full.

Doctors, though, have now proved that where mothers employ a method of preparing their breasts which not only strengthens the milk glands, but also stretches the milk ducts and tubes, they have been singularly free from feeding difficulties after their babies have arrived.

Soon after you quicken is a good time to begin your breast preparation. You will need two small basins, one containing hot water and the other containing cold water, with a separate wad of cotton wool in each. You will also need some good toilet soap and a towel. Once a day from the fifth month onwards (whether you are wearing nipple shells or not), splash the breasts with the hot and cold water alternately, using first hot, then cold, then hot, then cold and so on.   Finish the bathing

Fig 23

with the cold water (Fig. 23). Then, support each breast in turn with your free hand, and dry it carefully. Next, well soap your finger and thumb and massage each nipple separately, every now and again gripping its base gently, and with a light touch making three or four pincer-like movements. If the nipple tends to jerk forwards each time, you have the right action.

Continue this routine every day until you are between seven and eight months pregnant. Then add the following movement* to the others : slide the four fingers of each hand simultaneously down each side of each breast in turn, working the two thumbs down the front at the same time (Fig. 24). Next, bring thumb and fingers towards one another as they approach the ring of dark

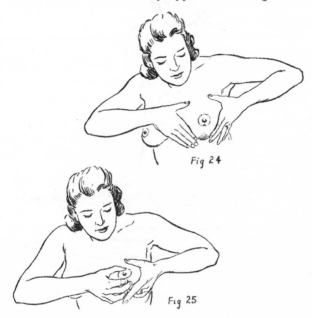

Fig 24

Fig 25

flesh in the centre. Repeat this movement three or four times and then give the dark ring a squeeze to imitate a baby's sucking (Fig. 25). Within a few days, if not at once, a spray of clearish fluid should jet out at each squeeze. The better the spray the more satisfied you can feel, because it shows you to what extent the milk ducts are becoming free, and you may be able to see, more or less, how many of them are functioning already.

*See note on page 50.

If you carry out this routine systematically before baby is born, breast feeding should be established with ease, the milk should flow steadily at feeding times and the likelihood of engorged or over-full breasts, with their resulting discomfort, should be reduced to the minimum.

Marital Relations

During the carrying months, sexual desire is heightened in some women, lessened in others.

Provided your pregnancy is running a normal course, with no sign of an impending miscarriage, there is no need to refrain from intercourse before the seventh month, but it is wise to avoid it during the few days when the periods would normally have fallen due.   After the seventh month it is much better to allow marital relations to cease until baby is four to six weeks old.

Always remember that as undue pressure on the abdomen is liable to cause discomfort, a change from the usual position is often found more satisfactory.   At all times during pregnancy, though, intercourse should be of an extra gentle nature and the mother's inclinations and wishes should receive the first consideration.

Once conception has occurred it is safe to presume that it cannot do so again for the time being.   If you have been in the habit of using contraceptives, there is no need to worry about them now until a month or two after the baby is born, at any rate.

Hygiene

Personal hygiene is, perhaps, more important during pregnancy than at any other time.   A comfortably warm bath should be taken frequently, and this should be followed by a good rub down and a sprinkle of talcum powder after drying.   Very hot baths and also as a rule, cold baths, should be avoided, but a tepid sponge down each morning is extremely health-giving.   If a bath is not always possible, let an all-over wash take its place.

Quite a number of expectant mothers worry unnecessarily because they are not sure if they may or may not wash their hair while they are carrying. You may do so as often as you wish, and you may visit your hairdresser for cutting, curling and permanent waving in precisely the same way as if you were not pregnant at all.

Bad for Baby

The effect of both alcohol and nicotine can reach an unborn baby through his mother's blood. When they do, nicotine may increase the rate of his heart-beat while alcohol in excess can affect his growth.

This does not mean that occasional smoking is going to be injurious to your child, or that you can never enjoy a glass of wine. But it does mean that if you smoke as a usual thing, you should only smoke now in strict moderation and without inhaling, and also that you are much better without spirits.

Bad for You

A bloodstained loss, discharges, severe pain or backache, abdominal cramp, bad sickness in the early months and sickness of any kind starting after the fourth month, blurred vision, swelling of the legs, hands or face, persistent sleeplessness, extreme thirst and frequent headaches ought not to be considered as normal. If you notice any of these signs while you are pregnant, see a doctor without delay, or tell your midwife who will ask a doctor to see you if this is necessary.

End of the Journey

An expectant mother who eats the right type of food, drinks sufficient fluid, lives an active, healthy life, pays attention to the usual rules of hygiene, visits her doctor or midwife regularly, avoids heavy smoking, and sees that she gets sufficient exercise and rest, should be able to preserve her figure, keep her hair soft and glossy, her nails in good condition and her teeth free from decay. And she should have a straightforward confinement and become the happy mother of a fine and healthy child.

Most mothers I find, who are expecting their first babies, like to know the symptoms of commencing labour beforehand—especially in view of the fact that odd pains (which are not true labour pains) are liable to be felt during the last two or three weeks of pregnancy.

To travel to a hospital or a nursing home, perhaps some distance away, or to call in your doctor or midwife only to find that it is a " false alarm " is both disappointing and vexing for you. It is much better to know what to expect when your little one is really ready to begin his important journey into this world. Then you will be able to recognise the heralding signs of true labour.

There are only three that you need bother about and they usually come in this order :—

1. Period-like pains.
2. A small period-like loss.
3. A gush of water which is not urine.

The pains are really contractions of the womb and it is much better to look upon them as such, remembering that each one, however slight, actually brings your baby just so much nearer to your arms.

Very often the pains begin low in the back, and work themselves round to the front of the abdomen and down the back of the thighs, but some mothers refer to the pain as being all round at the same time. One thing is quite certain and definite, though, and agreed upon by all. It is this : Each pain (or contraction) starts, increases in strength and then dies away. After an interval another one begins. That too, like its predecessor, increases in strength, diminishes and disappears. Then a third does exactly the same and so on. As time goes on though, the intervals between the pains become less while the pains themselves become stronger. But, there is always the same rhythmic sequence—start,

You should become the happy mother of a fine child.

increase, die away, rest ; start, increase, die away, rest.

When these pains begin you need not, as a rule, go to bed but you should inform your doctor or nurse. After that you can spend the time in making up baby's cot, airing his clothes and napkins and attending to any of the light home duties you particularly want to do.

If you are having your confinement in hospital, pack up your things and start off when the pains begin.

Now for the labour which starts with a loss of blood or a gush of water which is not urine.

Here, having informed your doctor or nurse, lie down on your bed while waiting for their arrival. If you have booked up at a hospital or nursing home then get some kind of conveyance to take you there. If you are able to lie down during that journey, so much the better.

One thing is quite certain. There is never any need to feel anxious or to be alarmed when labour commences. It is a perfectly natural happening remember, and the symptoms I have referred to occur at one stage or another in every baby's birth. If you follow the suggestions I have given before your doctor or nurse arrives, and put your faith in them completely once they are with you, you will find it will help them as much as it helps you. You and they then will form a team with this object in view, a happy mother and a splendid little baby.

* NOTE:—It is better not to try and learn this movement on your own, but rather to ask your doctor or midwife first to show you exactly how to do it.

CHAPTER III

BABY'S LAYETTE

ONE of the things the expectant mother loves best is planning her baby's layette. There is something essentially fascinating about tiny garments at any time, but when they are to be for your own little one, they become even more so, and getting the various items together one by one will give you many hours of delight.

If you like needlework and are able to sew or knit even moderately well you are sure to want to make everything that you can yourself. But, whether you do this or whether you buy, your aim will be to provide thoroughly up-to-date clothes, correct in detail, comfortable for baby and as pretty as they are practical.

The ideal baby clothes are light in weight yet sufficiently warm; roomy, but not clumsy; economical and at the same time not skimped. They are simple to make, easy to launder and should be lasting in wear.

About Layettes

There are three methods of clothing the new born baby to-day and it is largely a matter of personal choice as to which you select. In each case the under garments, the night clothes and shawls remain the same.

No. 1.—The Material Layette.

In this case baby wears a vest, napkin, petticoat, daygown and bootees with a knitted matinée coat when the weather is cold.

The Requirements for the Material Layette are :

3 vests (knitted or woollen material)
3–4 day gowns (of cotton, silk or muslin)

51

3-4 petticoats (of material similar to the nightgowns)
2 pairs of bootees
2 matinée coats (preferably knitted)
3-4 nightgowns
1 medium-sized shawl
1 large carrying shawl
12-18 Turkish towelling napkins
18 muslin napkins

No. 2.—The Knitted Layette.

If you choose a knitted layette you will dress your
baby in a vest, napkin, knitted jersey and pull-ups with
feet attached, and on cold days you will add a woollen
material matinée coat.

The Requirements for the Knitted Layette are :

3 vests (preferably of woollen material)
3 knitted jerseys
3 knitted pull-ups
2 matinée coats (preferably woollen material)
3-4 nightgowns
1 medium-sized shawl
1 large carrying shawl
12-18 Turkish towelling napkins
18 muslin napkins

No. 3.—The Economical Layette.

Here for the first three months baby wears his warm
soft nightgowns during the day as well as the night. From
nightgowns, he is put straight into first size short clothes.
Modern mothers prefer dresses and petticoats for a girl;
romper suits or tunic and knicker sets for a boy which
should last out the remainder of the first year.

The Requirements for the Economical Layette are:

3 vests
4 nightgowns
2 pairs of bootees
2 matinée coats (preferably knitted)
1 dress for special occasions of material similar to the
    nightgowns
1 medium-sized shawl
1 large carrying shawl
12-18 Turkish towelling napkins
18 muslin napkins

Whichever of the layettes you choose, you will need, in addition, one bandage about $3\frac{1}{2}$ inches wide. This is for wear until the navel has healed. After that no abdominal binder is necessary or advisable.

Non Essentials.

Gloves and bonnets are not worn as a regular thing until a child is old enough to sit up in his pram, and only then on cold days, so they have not been included. But if your baby is to be born in winter, you can add a soft bonnet and two pairs of fingerless mittens if you like. Pilches are not needed at first. Napkins put on carefully look very neat and the extra layer of the pilch is apt to over-heat child.

Materials

Day gowns can be of voile, muslin, silk, cotton or, for cold weather, nun's veiling. Rayon does not wear very well and nylon is not very suitable because it does not always allow good ventilation.

Nightgowns and petticoats should be of a similar material. A soft, loosely woven flannel or flannel mixture is best for both. Avoid flannelette. It is highly inflammable and this makes it dangerous.

Vests can be either knitted in silk and wool or in pure wool, or you can buy wool-woven vests.

Jersey and pull-up sets and also the bootees may be knitted in 3-ply wool, or like the vests a silk and wool mixture can be used for them.

Matinée coats are better knitted if you are dressing baby in petticoats and gowns (as in the first layette) or in nightgowns (as in the third layette). But, if baby is to wear the all-knitted suits (mentioned in the second layette), then woollen material matinée coats will keep him warmer and be more serviceable, you will find.

Angora and similar fluffy wools should not be used for any of baby's things. It is very heating and there is always the risk that bits of fluff will be swallowed.

Good Styles for Baby

Vests should be sufficiently long and have small sleeves. Some vests are of wrap-over variety ; some have a three-button front opening and high neck ; others fasten with a ribbon drawstring round the neck. Vests with V-necks are not suitable because they tend to gape as the child grows, and in doing so they fail to keep the chest dry from dribbling later on.

I advise mothers to sew a cotton tab to the front bottom edge of each vest to pin it down to the napkin. This saves the vests from riding up and leaving a gap where baby can feel the cold. Get size 2 in vests from the start. Smaller ones are so quickly outgrown.

Nightgowns which open right down the back are easy to put on and can be spread out to prevent them from getting wet. I like them to fasten with buttons and button holes from neck to waist, and then be free after that. They should be about 24 inches to 26 inches long.

Barras and back flannels are seldom used in these days. Little petticoats, which are much more satisfactory and certainly more comfortable for baby, have for the main part taken their place. Petticoats with shoulder openings are nicest but a back opening can be used. Petticoats are generally one inch shorter than the gowns.

Day gowns can be quite short from the first—18 to 22 inches is a good length. This saves shortening later on, for all that is needed is a tuck here and there, and you have the short clothes all ready. Gowns can be in any style or colour you fancy, but most mothers prefer white though some have one white, one pink and one blue dress. Touches of embroidery always add charm.

The bootees should have long tops so that they will keep baby's legs as well as his feet warm. They should be plenty large in the feet.

Making the Clothes

If you make some or all of baby's clothes yourself, you

will not only save money but you will also derive a great deal of pleasure from the work, and have the satisfaction of watching dainty little garments grow under your fingers as a result of your own labours. There are so many excellent patterns on the market that a few words as to the various good points to look for will be useful.

Both day and night gowns should have deep hems and if possible shoulder tucks to allow for growth. Those cut all in one will last longer than those with yolks, because as baby grows the yolk becomes tight across the chest and then the garment has to be discarded before it otherwise would be.

Set-in sleeves always look nice, and so long as the armhole is big enough they are very suitable, but a magyar style is easier to make and it is simple to launder. Raglan sleeves are excellent. They are roomy, comfortable and neat.

A plain neck is much more sensible than one with lace or frills which get wrinkled and soon become irritating. There should be a six-inch opening at the back of the gowns finished with small buttons and cut button holes. These are easier to fasten than the loops.

For Economy

If you want to be very economical, then by cutting your material according to Diagram I on page 56 you will get four nightgowns and four petticoats from 6 yards of 30-inch wide baby flannel. Follow Diagram II on page 57 and you will be able to cut four dresses from 3 yards of 36-inch material and have a small strip over at the end. If you decide on material matinée coats, then Diagram III on page 58 shows you how to get two little coats out of a remnant 36 inches wide and $\frac{1}{2}$ yard long.

The Petticoats and Nightgowns.

First of all cut yourself a paper pattern from a stout piece of paper to the measurements given. Fold your

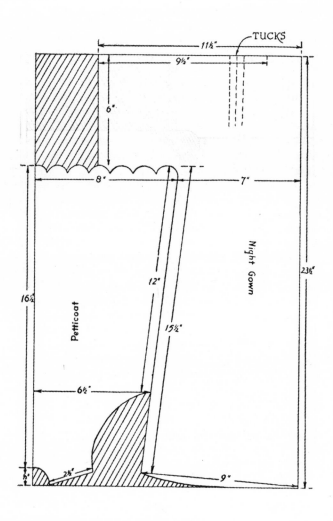

DIAGRAM I.

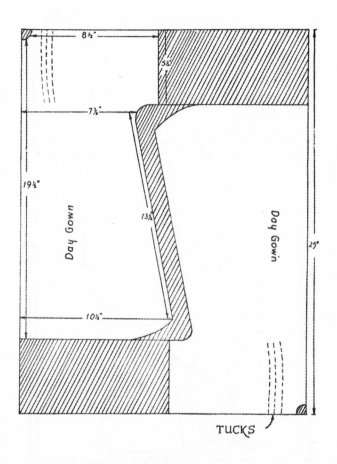

8½"

5⅜"

7⅞"

19½"

Day Gown

13½"

10½"

25"

Day Gown

TUCKS

DIAGRAM II

57

material in half lengthways and cut four times with the centre of the nightdress pattern against the fold, and the centre of the petticoat pattern against the selvedges. This will give you four nightdress-fronts and eight petti-coat back pieces. These eight must be joined by a neat seam down the centre back. *Then reverse the pattern* so that the petticoat centre lies to the fold, and the night-

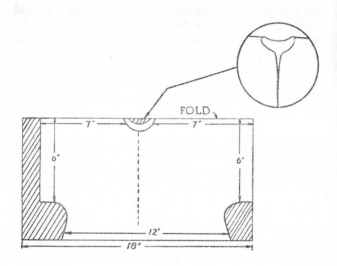

DIAGRAM III.

dress centre to the selvedges. Cut out another four times. You will then have four petticoat fronts without a seam, and eight nightgown-back pieces which are going to be open down the back in any case.

Join each petticoat up the sides, stitching a quarter of an inch from the edges of the material. Turn back the raw edges and herring-bone neatly down. Bind the arms, neck, shoulders and bottom with binding or ribbon.

Sew two small buttons on to each shoulder back, and work button-holes to match on the fronts of the shoulders.

Join the nightgown backs to the nightgown front with a narrow seam on each shoulder. Then make two or three small tucks where indicated by the dotted lines. Join side and underarm seams in one. Bind the neck and the sleeves at the wrists. Next, either face or turn in a quarter of an inch right down the right hand back piece, and half an inch on the corresponding left hand one and stitch neatly. Arrange for the left side to overlap the right, and sew six buttons on right back at regular intervals from neck to waist. Work button-holes to match in the left overlap. Turn up the bottom and from material left over, select a piece three inches square to stitch on as a tiny pocket for baby's own wisp of a handkerchief.

The Daygowns.

You can cut these out according to Diagram II and utilise the shaded parts for neck and sleeve bands, waist bands and facing the placket openings at the back. The dresses are made up like the nightgowns except that French seaming (or a run and fell seam) takes the place of the herring boning and the backs of the dresses are closed from the waistline to the hem. Babies dresses always look very much prettier for a touch of embroidery here and there.

The Matinée Coats.

These you can cut out to the measurements given in Diagram III. Join the sides and underarm seams in one, and then cut up the front of each coat from the lower centre edge to the neck. Bind the neck, both fronts (right and left), round the bottom and the sleeve edges with ribbon to match or, if you prefer, to contrast. Or, instead of binding the edges at the neck, you can make a little collar from pieces left over.

The Knitted Garments

Baby's Vest.

Materials. 4 oz. of 3-ply wool should make 4 vests. One pair of No. 8 knitting-needles. A little ribbon.

Back and front alike. Cast on 56 stitches very loosely and work in knit 2, purl 2 rib for 8 inches. Then knit 5 rows plain. Next row : Cast off 38, knit 18, and then work in plain knitting for 2 inches on these 18 stitches. Cast off. This completes the front and the whole of the right shoulder. Knit the back and the left shoulder to match. The sleeves : Cast on 36 stitches and work in knit 2, purl 2, rib for 5 rows. Continue in plain knitting until the work measures 1½ inches from the commencement. Increase 1 stitch at the end of each row until there are 44 stitches on the needle. Cast off. To make up : Press. Fold each shoulder piece in half and sew each to the other side of the vest in their respective places. Set in the sleeves, and then join the sleeve and underarm seams. Crochet a row of double crochet all round the neck. Then work a row of holes thus : *2 chain, miss 1 double crochet, 1 double crochet into the next and repeat from *. Thread a ribbon through the holes just made to draw up the neck and tie in front.

The Matinée Coat.

Materials. 3 oz. of 3-ply wool will make 2 coats. One pair of No. 8 knitting-needles. Embroidery silk. Ribbon.

Back and front are knitted in one. Cast on 60 stitches for the back and work in moss stitch (1st row knit 1, purl 1 ; 2nd row, the reverse, that is you purl the knit stitch and knit the purl one all along) for 12 rows. Change to stocking stitch (1st row knit, 2nd row purl) and continue until the work measures 8 inches from the commencement. Next row, stocking stitch 20 and place these stitches on a spare needle ; cast off 20 ; stocking stitch 20. Turn and work backwards and forwards on these 20 stitches for 8 rows. Cast on 14 stitches at the neck edge, and knit down the front, working 8 stitches in moss stitch on the front edge to form a border. Continue until this is the same length as the back. Then work in moss stitch for 12 rows. Cast off. Join the wool at the edge of the other shoulder and work the second front to match. The sleeves : Cast on 40 stitches and work in moss stitch for 12 rows. Continue in stocking stitch until the work measures 4 inches from the commencement. Increase 1 stitch at the end of every row until there are 50 stitches on the needle. Cast off and work the second sleeve to match. To make up : Press. Sew each sleeve into place and then join up the underarm and sleeve seams all in one. Work 2 rows of double crochet all round and embroider a tiny pattern down the two fronts. Stitch back both fronts at the neck to make reveres. Attach ribbon to fasten.

The Smaller Shawl.

Materials. 2 oz. of 2-ply wool. Two No. 8 knitting needles.

Cast on 131 stitches very loosely. Knit in moss stitch for 4 inches. Next row moss stitch along for 4 inches, then work in plain knitting until within 4 inches of the end of the row, and moss stitch those 4 inches. (For moss stitch : 1st row knit 1, purl 1 all along. 2nd row the reverse. That is, purl the knit stitch and knit the purl stitch.) Continue until the work is four inches short of being a perfect square. Then moss stitch for those four inches and cast off very loosely. This forms a plain square centre with a moss stitch border. Pin out the work on an ironing board and press very lightly.

The Carrying Shawl.

Materials. 8 oz. of 2-ply wool. Two No. 8 knitting needles.

Cast on 261 stitches and proceed as for the smaller

shawl but make the border 12 inches all round instead of 4 inches.   When finished, press lightly.

The Jersey and Pull-ups.

Materials.   4 oz. of 3-ply wool.   One pair of No. 9 knitting needles.   Medium sized crochet hook.   Four small buttons.   Ribbon.

The Jersey.   Front and back alike.   Cast on 52 stitches loosely and work in knit 1, purl 1, rib for 2½ inches.   Change to moss stitch (1st row, knit 1, purl 1 ; 2nd row, the reverse.   That is purl the knit stitch and knit the purl stitch all along).   When the work measures 7 inches from the commencement shape the armhole by casting off 3 stitches at the beginning of the next two rows and then knitting 2 together at the beginning of the next 6 rows.   Continue in moss stitch until the work measures 9 inches.   Next row, moss stitch 11 stitches. Cast off 18.   Moss stitch 11.   Work 1 inch on these 11 stitches.   Cast off.   Join the wool and work 1 inch on the other 11 stitches.   Cast off.   This forms the back. Knit the front to match.   The sleeves : Cast on 28 stitches, and work in knit 1, purl 1, rib for 2 inches. Change to moss stitch.   Increase 1 stitch at both ends of the 3rd row and every following 4th row until there are 40 stitches.   Continue working on these 40 stitches until the work measures 6 inches.   Then shape the armhole by casting off 3 stitches at the beginning of each of the next 2 rows and knitting 2 together at the beginning of every following row until only 17 stitches remain. Cast off.   Work another sleeve to match.   To make up : Press the work lightly.   Sew up the sleeve seams and the side seams of the jersey.   Sew the sleeves into the armholes, arranging for the front shoulder pieces of the jersey to slighty overlap the back.   Sew two small buttons on to each back shoulder piece.   Join the wool at one shoulder and work in crochet from shoulder to shoulder on both the jersey front and back :   1st row, 2 double

crochet, 2 chain. Repeat. 2nd row, 1 double crochet
into the loop made with 2 chain of the first row, 3 chain,
join with slip stitch into the 1st chain. Repeat. Thread
a ribbon through the holes round the neck, and use the
same holes on the shoulder pieces as buttonholes for the
buttons. Turn up the little cuffs.

The Pull-ups. Cast on 72 stitches and work in knit 1,
purl 1, rib for 6 rows. Next row, knit 1, purl 1, * make
1 by putting the wool forward, knit 2 together, knit 1,
purl 1, knit 1, purl 1, repeat from * to the end of the row.
Rib for another 6 rows and then change to moss stitch.
With the right side of the work towards you, 1st row :
moss stitch 12, turn and work back. 2nd row : moss
stitch 24, turn and work back. 3rd row : moss stitch
36, turn and work back. 4th row : moss stitch 48, turn
and work back. 5th row : moss stitch 60, turn and
work back. Continue in moss stitch until $5\frac{1}{2}$ inches in
length has been worked in this stitch. (For the second
leg the work is the same, but start with the wrong side
of the work towards you.) Then decrease 1 stitch at
both ends of the needle in every row until 42 stitches
remain. Decrease a further 1 stitch at each end of every
8th row until 36 stitches remain. Put the first 12 stitches
and the last 12 stitches on safety-pins and work on the
centre 12 stitches for 2 inches. Decrease 1 at both ends
of the next 4 rows, leaving 4 stitches. Break off the
wool and join at the outer edge. Knit the first 12
stitches, pick up and knit 20 stitches along the instep
piece, knit the 4 stitches of the front, pick up and knit
20 stitches along the other side of the instep, knit 12 (68
stitches). Work 16 rows in plain knitting. Next row :
knit 2 together, knit 24, knit 2 together, knit 12, knit 2
together, knit 24, knit 2 together. Next row : knit 2
together, knit 23, knit 2 together, knit 10, knit 2 together,
knit 23, knit 2 together. Continue decreasing thus until
48 stitches remain. Next row : knit 24. Place the two
needles side by side, and cast off both needles together.

Knit a second leg, *with the shapings reversed*. To make up. Press lightly. Sew up leg, back and front seams. Thread ribbon ties through the holes at the waist.

Bootees.

Materials. Oddments of 2-ply or 3-ply wool. One pair of No. 10 knitting-needles. A little ribbon.

Cast on 36 stitches. Work in knit 1, purl 1, rib for 4½ inches. Next row : * knit 1, make 1, knit 2 together, repeat from * to make holes for the ribbon. Then knit 3 rows plain. Next row : knit 24, turn and knit 12 back. Then knit backwards and forwards on these 12 stitches for 1½ inches. Pick up 12 stitches along both sides of the centre panel and then the 12 stitches at both ends (60 stitches). Knit the next 12 rows. Then decrease 1 stitch at each end and 2 stitches in the centre of each of the next 4 rows. Next row : knit to the centre, place both needles together and cast off.

Making a Sleeping Bag

A sleeping-bag is a most useful accessory especially when baby is older and kicks off the bedclothes.

It is very easy to make from an old soft blanket, or two cot blankets. Cut out the back and front according to Diagram IV, allowing small turnings on the outside seams. Then sew up the side and underarm seams, and seam the right shoulder. The left shoulder is left open and it fastens with four large buttons and button holes. Bind the neck and both edges of this shoulder with ribbon. Sew the 4 buttons to the back and work button holes to correspond along the front of the shoulder opening. Next bind the sleeves and right round the bottom. Work eight button holes along the front bottom edge and sew 8 buttons to the *inside* of the back piece. Or make the back of the bag a few inches longer than the front, so that it folds over and buttons on to the front. In this case, sew the buttons on the *outside* of the front piece.

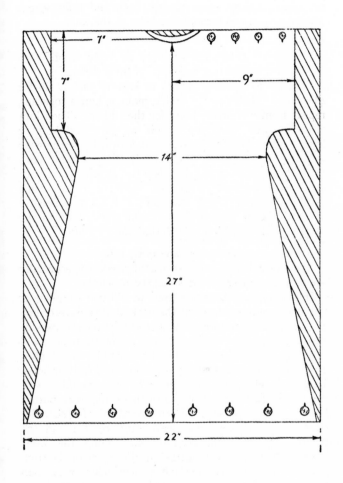

DIAGRAM IV.

Making the Napkins

These you will find very easy to make. You will need 8 yards of 24 inch wide Turkish towelling to make a dozen napkins. Cut this into 12 pieces each 24 inches square and bind the two cut edges on each napkin neatly with white tape. The muslin napkins are made up double, so for twenty-four of these you will need 41½ yards of material. Cut this into strips 31 inches wide by 61 inches long, fold each one in half and stitch half an inch from the cut edges leaving a small opening on one side. Turn the napkin inside out and stitch right round the finished square.

Likely Presents

Most mothers receive several little gifts once relatives and friends know a baby is on the way, and amongst those most popular to give are matinée coats, bootees, daygowns, bibs, bonnets, gloves and small shawls. So bear this in mind when getting the layette together.

You will also require a pram set, consisting of coat, leggings and mittens for when baby goes out, but as it will not be wanted at first you can wait till after baby is born and get it then if you have not had one given to you.

CHAPTER IV

AT HOME OR IN HOSPITAL ?

THERE is one very important thing you must decide quite early in your pregnancy. It is whether you are going to have a baby at home, in a nursing home, in a maternity home or in a hospital.

In these days midwives and beds in hospitals and maternity homes are booked up months ahead, so the sooner you are able to get this point settled, the better. Not only that. A mother always feels more contented in her own mind once she has the necessary arrangements for her confinement well in hand.

Talking It Over

It is best to look at the question from all angles first, and talk it over with your husband. Weigh up the various advantages and disadvantages that strike you, consider your own wishes and inclinations and then discuss the amount of money you are able to afford.

You can either book with a doctor as a private patient, or you can become a patient under the National Health Service where all medical, dental, midwifery and hospital services are without charge, but you may have to pay a little towards your medicine.

If you or your husband fulfil the contribution conditions under the National Insurance Scheme you will be entitled to cash maternity benefits. As these must be claimed within certain time limits, you are strongly advised to get an official leaflet and the claim form from your local Pensions and National Insurance Office as soon as you can, and study it carefully.

There are broadly, nine alternatives open to you. They are:

(1) Your own home (as a private patient).

(2) Someone else's home (as a private patient).

(3) Your own home (as a National Health Service patient).

(4) Somebody else's home (as a National Health Service patient).

(5) A private nursing-home.

(6) Maternity home (under the National Health Service).

(7) A private ward in a hospital.

(8) Public ward in a hospital (under the National Health Service).

(9) In certain cases, a private ward in a hospital (under the National Health Service).

At Home

Here you will be amongst your own surroundings—an important factor with many mothers. Provided there are the necessary conveniences (the ideal are a bathroom, indoor sanitation, plenty of hot and cold water) and your case is a straightforward one, there is much to be said for having your baby at home.

Question of Costs.

If you decide to have a private doctor to attend you at home when you have baby, there will be his fees to consider. These vary so greatly that it is best to discuss this matter with him before asking him definitely to take on your case. The fees would include ante-natal care, attendance at the confinement and for about fourteen days afterwards and one final visit at the end of six weeks to ensure that everything has gone back to normal. If an anaesthetist is required his fees would be extra.

The fee for a private nurse living in is generally on a weekly or monthly basis with an allowance for laundry and all travelling expenses both to and from the case.

She is usually engaged for three to four weeks. A visiting nurse working under a doctor, charges less—usually so much per visit.

There will be extras in the form of the chemist's bill, additional laundry, heating if the weather is cold, and help in the home if you have no maid or home help to look after this for you. In many cases, though, some member of the family is only too pleased to come along and housekeep while the new mother is in bed, and is often willing to stay on until the baby is four or five weeks old. This is an admirable solution to the domestic problem, where it can be arranged, so never hesitate to approach your mother or mother-in-law, or perhaps an aunt who has no strong home ties.

What You Will Need.

For a home confinement, the following is a list of the things you will probably require. Many of them can be borrowed from the kitchen and bathroom; a few can be borrowed from friends; the others will have to be bought specially for the occasion.

1 accouchement sheet (from the chemist)
1 mackintosh sheet to cover the mattress, or several sheets of stout brown paper can be used to cover the mattress as protection
1 small mackintosh sheet about 36 inches long by 24 (This can afterwards be used for baby's cot)
3 or 4 old sheets freshly laundered
1 old blanket freshly laundered
2 dozen large and 2 dozen smaller sanitary towels
1 bottle of midwifery antiseptic
2 kettles
2 large jugs
8 bowls (pudding basins of varying sizes will do)
1 wash hand basin
1 slop pail with lid
1 bed pan
1 bottle of methylated spirits
2 boxes of matches
4 to 6 hand towels
several large safety pins
1 fresh tablet of soap

    1 new nail brush
    1 medicine glass
      several clean newspapers
    1 hot-water bottle with a good cover
    2 small firm tables
      Baby's cot and clothes

In addition, ask your nurse whether you should obtain
a sterilised maternity drum from the chemist. The
better ones are usually packed with sterilised gowns,
masks and towels as well as dressings and in these drums
many of the articles, such as gowns and towels, are
returnable after use, when a proportionate refund of the
purchase money is made, thus reducing the initial outlay.
On no account must a maternity drum be opened by
anyone except your doctor or nurse.

For your own use you will require:

    3–4 nightgowns
      1 bed jacket
      1 dressing gown
      1 pair of bedroom slippers
      1 bath towel
      1 hand towel
      1 nail brush and soap
        Toothbrush and dentifrice
        Hairbrush and comb

Preparing the Room.

Your room should be thoroughly turned out a full
week before your appointed time. Each day afterwards,
it should be wiped over with a cloth wrung out of
disinfectant.

As a new mother generally sits up for the greater part
of each day, four or five pillows, a bed rest and if possible,
a bed table will add to your comfort while you are in bed,
Try to arrange for a gas ring, an electric kettle or a trivet
at the fireplace for boiling up supplies of water. A good
deal of hot water will be needed. In your room there
should be good artificial lighting with a small hand or
table lamp, in addition if possible to the ceiling or wall
lighting.

For the actual confinement a fairly high single bed is more convenient than a double one. If there is any tendency for the mattress to sag in the middle, this is easily corrected by slipping two or three boards across the framework of the bed under the hair mattress and over the wire or the springs.

For the birth make up your bed like this (Fig. 26):

First lay	1 long protective mackintosh sheet over the hair mattress
Then place	1 under blanket over this mackintosh.
Next have	1 strong cotton sheet, and
Over that	1 small strip of mackintosh about 2 ft. in width and 3 ft. 6 ins. long. This goes across the centre part of the bed,
Covered by	1 sheet over this, folded double and tucked in at both sides,
And finally	the top sheet, blankets and covering.

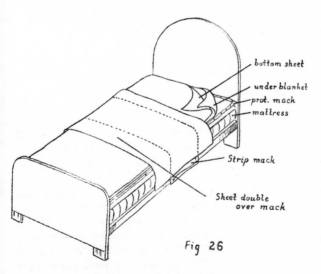

bottom sheet
under blanket
prot. mack
mattress

Strip mack

Sheet double over mack

Fig 26

It is a great help to a doctor and nurse to find one or two small tables have been set aside exclusively for their use along with a wash-hand basin, soap, hand towel and nailbrush.   Boil the nailbrush, place it in a scalded bowl, cover with fresh boiling water and then put a clean inverted saucer over all.

If your bedroom floor is covered with a carpet, a clean dust sheet or newspapers should be laid down to protect it from accidental splashes and to prevent any dust rising from it.   When the confinement is over the paper is, of course, removed along with anything else brought in for the occasion.

For a confinement in someone else's private house the requirements will for all practical purposes be the same, except that extra help in the home may or may not be your responsibility, according to mutual arrangements.

National Health Service.

Under the National Health Service every expectant and nursing mother is entitled to the services of a doctor, dentist, midwife and health visitor, or hospital services if necessary, without charge.

As soon as you think you are pregnant you should go to your family doctor, the midwife or the Welfare Centre for confirmation of your pregnancy, and then make full use of the services provided for you.

For a Home Confinement.

Your family doctor will arrange to look after you himself if you are to have your baby at home, or he will suggest a doctor in the neighbourhood who will be willing to undertake your maternity care.   Your maternity doctor will tell you when to come and see him for ante-natal and post-natal examinations, and will attend your confinement, with the midwife, if he thinks it advisable.

The midwife will provide her share of your ante-natal care, sometimes at the ante-natal clinic in a Maternity and Child Welfare Centre (where you may also meet the health visitor) or in your own home.   She will discuss the arrangements for the confinement with you, take charge in the absence of a doctor, and will call in a doctor should his services be required.   She will attend you during your confinement, and regularly for about a fortnight after, and you may be sure she is both capable and competent.

As soon as your pregnancy is confirmed, you should book a midwife, either at her home or through the Welfare Centre, where you can discuss any problems with her during your pregnancy.

If you need a home help during or after your confinement (whether it is at home or in hospital), ask the midwife or the Welfare Centre to put you in touch with the home help service.   Where this is available, a charge to cover the cost will be made by the local health authority, according to your ability to pay.

Nursing and Maternity Homes

Perhaps you have not the convenience for having baby at home.   You may not have the room; there may be no one to see to the meals; to get the extra hot water needed and do the washing up that will be required.   Or, maybe you feel it would be a rest and a relief from the little worries to go away and have baby where there would be no cares.

In that case you will probably decide to have your confinement in a private nursing home, where you will be relieved of all the housekeeping, the preparation of your room, and getting together all or some of the things mentioned in the list for a home confinement.   As a rule the matron of the home orders the maternity drum on the mother's behalf.

Visiting hours in nursing homes are hardly restricted at all, so it is quite likely you will be allowed to see a friend each afternoon, and your husband or a near relative at other times as well.

The Question of Costs.

Three weeks is the average time for a mother to stay

C*

in a private nursing home. The weekly charge varies with the status of the establishment concerned, its locality and the position and size of the room occupied. For instance, a large front room on the first floor would be considerably more expensive than a small back room.

Nursing home fees usually include all nursing unless for some reason a special nurse or one not shared with anyone else is required, light and heating, all your own meals (but not visitors' meals where they are given), and the use of bed linen. They do not include the doctor's and anaesthetist's accounts, the chemist's bills and the maternity drum. Mother's and baby's personal laundry is generally extra as well.

What You will Need.

Nursing homes also vary greatly as to their individual requirements. It is best therefore to ask the matron at the one you think of going to, to give you a list of what you should take in. The usual necessities are:—

For yourself:

1 dressing gown
1 pair of bedroom slippers
4 nightdresses
1 bed jacket
2 hand towels
2 bath towels
  Hairbrush and comb
  Any other toilet articles you fancy

For baby:

All his clothes and napkins, but not the cot or cot blankets unless you wish

The following articles for his toilet:

1 cake of baby soap
1 tin of baby powder
1 packet of large rustless safety pins
1 reel of white cotton size 24
1 needle of suitable size for the cotton
1 soft hairbrush
2 bath towels

These are usually put into his own basket, which should have a well-fitting lid and may be lined to match the colour scheme of his cot and other accessories.

National Health Service.

Maternity homes within the National Health Service are liable to vary a little in different districts. Many of the larger ones have a resident doctor, others are staffed by midwives who call in a doctor should one be needed. There are no fees liable in the ordinary way, but in some it is possible to have a private room if one is available by paying for it. The treatment and care given to a mother and her baby is often very similar to what she might expect in a private nursing home. Many maternity homes have their own ante-natal clinics. At others, patients who have booked there receive their ante-natal care at a hospital or a welfare clinic to which the maternity home may be attached. These maternity homes accept maternity cases only. Private nursing homes may take in other cases besides maternity ones.

Hospital Confinements

In most hospitals there is always one and often two or three (or more) resident doctors who live in the building and one of them is therefore always on call. In addition there are such facilities as X-rays always available.

Private Wards.

A private ward in a hospital is very much like a private room in a nursing home. The visiting hours for patients in the private wards are very liberal. You would probably be allowed to see your relatives and friends every afternoon and some evenings too, but of course these arrangements do vary in different institutions.

Mothers are usually expected to take in the same things with them as they would when going into a private nursing home and outside arrangements usually have to be made for the mother's and baby's laundry, though some hospitals wash the baby's clothes and napkins on the premises or send them out to be done.

The usual length of stay is three to four weeks and all fees are paid direct to the hospital authorities.

Public Wards.

Public wards in a maternity hospital or the Maternity Department of a general or women's hospital vary in size. They can contain two to twenty beds.

The visiting hours are, naturally, very much more restricted than in the private wards of the hospital, or a private room in a maternity home, but there is no set rule, however. Some institutions have somewhat longer or more frequent visiting periods than others. Hospitals have a labour ward attached to their maternity unit where the actual birth takes place, and when it is over the mother is carried or wheeled back to a bed in a ward of other new mothers.

What You Will Need.

It is best to make exact inquiries beforehand as to what you should take with you because as a general rule the mother wears the hospital nightgowns and bed jackets —the latter frequently being of one pattern and colour to match the decorations of the ward—and clothes are loaned to the baby for his stay. This means that the only items you will require of your own are:

    1 toothbrush
    Other toilet articles
    Dressing gown
    Slippers (even these may not be needed)

For baby, one set of baby clothes and a large shawl. The baby clothes are to take your baby home in. A " set " consists of:

    1 vest
    1 day-night-gown (or 1 petticoat and 1 dress)
    1 matinée coat
    2 napkins
    1 pair of bootees

A set of baby clothes.

Sometimes the set of baby clothes and the shawl are not brought to the hospital until the morning of the mother's departure, but this also is a thing to make enquiries about shortly before the birth is due.

Allocation of Beds

Hospital bookings are always very heavy indeed. Priority is given (1) to cases with complications or where a difficult labour is anticipated, (2) to cases where there is inadequate convenience in the mother's home, and (3) to women having their first babies.

Cases where it is medically necessary will always be admitted, but the allotting of beds for all other straightforward cases may vary in different institutions.

It follows, therefore, that quite a number of mothers who would have liked a hospital confinement will be disappointed. Should this happen in your case, there is no need to feel worried. Statistics show that a large percentage of the total number of births in any one year take place in the home and a great number of these are attended at the actual confinement by midwives only. When one looks round and sees the satisfactory health of both the mothers and the children, one could wish for no finer testimony.

CHAPTER V

KEEP YOURSELF WELL

As an expectant mother it is very important that you keep yourself really well. In fact, you should feel and look better in health now than ever before. Nevertheless, there are various discomforts and worries or even upsets which sometimes appear ; and small though they may and should be, they can be annoying and disagreeable if you do not know how to deal with them, and if you have no idea as to what is normal and what is not.

Nausea and Vomiting

You must not think that just because you are pregnant you must, therefore, suffer from sickness or a feeling of sickness which is often present during the second and third months, and which may appear as morning sickness, evening sickness or odd-time sickness. If it should appear, though, remember it is always made worse by anxiety, constipation, unsuitable food, pressure round the bust and waist, getting over-tired, a deficiency in calcium and by the mistaken idea that every expectant mother is sick and therefore you must be the same.

Where it does occur, it is generally caused by the sudden flooding of the mother's blood stream with waste from her rapidly developing baby. After a few weeks her system adjusts itself to coping with the new and double duty of dealing with the used products from the bodies of two people—mother and baby—but just at first it is thrown out of rhythm, as it were. That is why, in the cases where this sickness does appear, it so often starts during the second month, when the presence of the child is beginning to be noticed. But the vomiting should never at any time be bad, and it should have disappeared completely before the fourth month is out.

To help it, try and arrange to get a little extra rest. Perhaps you can get to bed a little earlier for a few nights. Have your supper in bed when you can manage it. Sip a cup of hot well-sweetened tea or take some fruit juice and water to which you have added glucose or sugar before getting up in the morning, and drink this lying flat—not sitting up. Then remain lying quietly for ten minutes before rising and dressing slowly.

Instead of ordinary meals, take small snacks at frequent intervals during the day and avoid a heavy supper in the evening. Arrange your diet to suit your present needs and make sure that it is really supplying you with foods that are rich in calcium and in Vitamin B. Some of the best are sheep's liver, milk, fruit, green salads, most vegetables, practically all cereals, cheese, butter and eggs. Some doctors always recommend supplementing the natural calcium intake by sodium-calcium lactate taken by mouth two or three times a day half an hour before meals.

If you are threatened with sickly feelings you will find it a help to omit all fried foods and hot buttered or hot margarined toast, and possibly to give up meat and eggs for a few days and replace these with extra salads and fruit. Very often a pinch of bi-carbonate of soda stirred into all liquids will help to dispel nausea. Sucking some plain, boiled, sugar sweets or a stick of the old fashioned black liquorice are two other remedies well worth trying.

Where pregnancy sickness is bad, where it persists despite your efforts to check it, or where it begins after or continues past the fourteenth week, or so, always consult a doctor at once since the trouble may be an indication that the kidneys and liver are being overtaxed and are, as a result, having difficulty in getting rid of waste materials from the body and the blood. You should never neglect this. If you do, there is fear that baby's health may suffer as well as your own. Prompt medical treatment though, will nearly always relieve the condition before it gets bad.

Indigestion

Indigestion may be the result of a badly-balanced diet, or of taking too large a meal at one sitting, or of eating too heavy a meal at night, or too many dried foods. Constipation, too, sometimes causes the trouble. Correct these, and the indigestion generally disappears quickly. If necessary, a simple anti-acid such as a little magnesia is helpful, or a few drops of peppermint essence in water, or a peppermint sweet; but the main thing is to correct the diet. Then the indigestion should go.

Backache

Backache is liable to occur any time after the first few weeks. It may be due to a drag on some of the large internal muscles. When this is so, it is relieved by wearing an uplifting maternity belt arranged so that it takes some of the weight of the abdomen. You can easily prove this for yourself if you place both hands under and in front of the abdomen and lift it gently in an upward direction. If it gives you relief, then the trouble ought to disappear when a maternity belt is worn.

Backache can also be due to wearing the wrong type of shoes where the heels are either too high or too low.

Constipation

Constipation is liable to occur during pregnancy where it has not been troublesome or even present before. Where it already exists, having a baby always seems to make it worse. Strong aperients, medicines containing aloes, castor oil and salts should be avoided unless these have been medically ordered.

Once again, though, diet becomes important, and it should be arranged so as to provide adequate fluid and an additional supply of Vitamin B. The following foods are rich in this vitamin: Wholemeal bread, dried peas, beans and lentils, oatmeal, germ of wheat, yeast extract, most nuts and hard and soft fish roes.

Fruit is always helpful in combatting the constipation, prunes being particularly valuable. These may either be stewed, or provided they have been well soaked for twenty-four hours, eaten raw. If anything further is needed, syrup of figs, senna tea (make by soaking two to ten senna pods in water overnight) or 2-grain cascara tablets are amongst the most favoured remedies. It is better not to take medicinal liquid paraffin on your own because it may interfere with the assimilation of vitamins.

Piles

Unfortunately the appearance of piles is not uncommon during the carrying months. Some expectant mothers seem more prone to the complaint than others. In bad cases, piles tend to make the confinement more painful. Therefore, everything possible should be done to alleviate the trouble in its early stages. At the first sign of a pile, it is a great help to bathe it with alternately very hot and very cold water for a few minutes two or three times a day and also after each bowel action.

After bathing, dry gently and apply a trace of calamine ointment. The condition should be mentioned to your doctor or midwife at your next visit. Constipation must be avoided where piles are present, and so, also, must frequent motions. Both tend to aggravate the condition.

Excessive Flow of Saliva

Although it can be rather worrying where it does appear, an excessive flow of saliva is not very common. In most of the cases it points to indigestion, so adopt the suggestions for correcting that trouble first and if anything further is needed try holding alternately very hot and very cold water in the mouth. A few sweet almonds eaten after meals are helpful if they are very well chewed, and so is sucking a small piece of ice.

Strong Movements

Because very violent movements on the baby's part may indicate the need for more calcium, this discomfort should be treated medically. At the same time, it must be remembered that as pregnancy advances, the movements naturally become more pronounced and more frequent, too. They should not, though, be sufficient to keep you awake at night, or cause distress during the day, and if they do either, you should see your doctor.

Varicose Veins

Now and again varicose veins appear for the first time during the carrying months, but where they were present before, they may tend to become troublesome.

In either case, anything which assists the circulation, helps the veins. For this reason, sit with your feet up whenever you can and try not to stand about for long intervals at a stretch. Take short, brisk walks and see that your maternity belt takes as much of baby's weight as possible so as to avoid any downward pressure on the big blood vessels running to and from the legs.

It is a help, too, to sleep with the legs a little higher than the rest of the body. This you can easily accomplish if you place a bolster, suitcase or similar object underneath the foot-end of the mattress on your bed.

Crêpe bandages, put on like a soldier's puttee before getting out of bed in the morning, provide excellent support, and these are not dear to buy ; or, for those who prefer, there are elastic stockings.

Any swelling round the front passage may be due to a small varicosed vein in that region. This trouble should always have a doctor's attention.

Irritation

Irritation in the region of the vulva—that is the fleshy part round the opening to the front passage—is occasionally a source of trouble. This should be reported to a doctor, but in the meantime you can bathe yourself with warm water to which you have added a teaspoonful of iodine to each pint of water. It is both simple and soothing, and it is quite safe. Often omitting all meat from the diet for a few days will give relief.

Skin Discomforts

There are two forms of skin discomfort which can worry an expectant mother. One is a tightness of the skin over the abdomen caused by the enlarging figure. The other, a persistent irritation of the skin (generally of the arms and legs) usually due to shortage of calcium.

The first is relieved by gently rubbing a little oil, cold cream or any form of grease into the skin two or three times a week. If from quite early in your pregnancy you make a practice of doing this regularly, it is very unlikely that you will suffer from this uncomfortable, taut, stretched feeling as the abdomen gets larger.

The second, persistent skin irritation, is relieved when additional calcium is taken, either in the form of tablets or by eating more of those foods which are naturally rich in it. Amongst the most useful in this way are : cheese, turnip-tops, black treacle, kale, watercress, dried figs, milk, brocolli, dried beans, lentils and spinach.

Cramp

Cramp in the legs is one of the troubles to which quite a number of pregnant women are prone especially after getting to bed at night, but lying with the legs stretched out as far as possible and the feet turned up until the toes point to the ceiling generally brings relief. Rubbing the calves each evening with a little simple oil (olive oil, salad oil, or even medicinal paraffin) is helpful too, but where such methods do not effect a cure, then a shortage of calcium is probably at the root of the trouble, and a course of calcium tablets will probably be ordered or, if you are taking them already, the dose may be increased.

Abdominal cramp, on the other hand, should be

reported to a doctor immediately.   It is one of the signs that a miscarriage may be threatening.

Heartburn

Heartburn is generally caused by taking food that is too rich.   Less fat and more sugar for a few days is indicated.   Eat crisp toast in place of bread, and a small slice of burnt toast if the attack is troublesome. Drink large amounts of warm water between meals, take your food as dry as possible, eat sparingly and give up salt.   Avoid sodamint and bicarbonate of soda (unless medically ordered) since both tend to increase the trouble next day, although they may afford temporary relief. Half a teaspoonful of white vinegar in a wineglassful of hot water, though, or a slice of lemon steeped in hot water, often proves a useful and simple cure.

Sleeplessness

If sleeplessness is troublesome or persistent it needs your doctor's attention.   If it is just an occasional occurrence, then tucking a small pillow under the abdomen will provide additional comfort and this alone often induces sleep.   A warm drink, too, is beneficial, and so, very often, is sleeping with the head raised on an additional pillow.   Make quite sure that you are warm enough in bed, slipping on a pair of bed socks if you are subject to cold feet.   If sleep still does not come, never mind, close your eyes and rest in the darkness, occupying your mind with pleasant thoughts and trying to relax every muscle in the body.   The quiet rest will do you just as much good if you are sensible about it, but if you work yourself up into a state of anxiety and annoyance, then you will be doing your nervous system harm, and you will be sure to feel more tired next day.

Swollen Legs

Swollen legs or ankles may be due to the additional

weight being carried.   They may also be due to varicose veins or, on the other hand, the swelling may be a sign that the kidneys are not functioning properly.

This is especially true when the discomfort is accompanied by sickness, trouble with the eyesight (such as a blurred vision, dimness of sight, flashes of light before the eyes, or perhaps, even, attacks of partial blindness), bad or persistent headaches, tired and sleepy feelings, or by puffiness of the hands, arms or face.   If you notice any one or more of these symptoms, the only wise course is to inform your doctor or midwife at once before things have time to get bad.   Do not be tempted to wait until your next visit is due.   Go right away, taking with you a sample of your urine in a perfectly clean bottle, so that they can test this and tell you exactly what to do to put things right again.

Sickness in the Later Months

Sickness in the later months should not be confused with the nausea and vomiting of the early ones when it is not uncommon and, unless severe, should be nothing to worry about.   Appearing after the sixteenth week or so, sickness is not normal and is a thing to see your doctor or midwife about immediately.

Excessive Thirst

The expectant mother ought not to be abnormally thirsty and if you feel you require much more to drink than the three or four pints of liquid daily, which is the ideal intake for you now, you should get medical advice and have your urine re-tested.

Intercourse

The question of intercourse during pregnancy is one which troubles many expectant mothers.   Some find they have more desire during this time, others less ; but most are uncertain as to whether it is wise for marital relations to continue, and if so, for how long.

The answer to this is, as we saw in Chapter II, that providing your pregnancy is running a normal course, and there is no sign of a miscarriage and no history of a previous one, intercourse may continue up to the seventh month, except during those few days each month when the periods would normally have fallen due.

If, though, in your particular case a miscarriage has threatened in this pregnancy, or has threatened or occurred during a previous one, then you should abstain from marital relations until you have spoken to your doctor on the subject and obtained his advice.

In any case, from the seventh month onwards it is wiser for you to sleep alone. The reason for this is two-fold. Firstly, the womb and the surrounding parts are getting ready for baby's birth, and are better without stimulation of any kind. Secondly, there is the possibility of introducing germs (harmless enough at all other times) however careful and particular you may be. Although in many cases they certainly do no harm at all, it is better if they are not present, and as the life of the average germ is extremely short, the two-month interval provides ample time for them all to have disappeared.

Discharges

A slight whitish discharge is not uncommon during pregnancy. Indeed, most expectant mothers see this, and it is nothing to worry about. But, during the whole of the carrying time, right up until your labour commences, there should be no coloured or bloodstained one.

If there is, or if there is severe pain, a persistent bearing down sensation, or cramp in the abdomen, it may mean that a miscarriage is threatened. The thing to do in such cases as these is to retire to bed immediately and send for your doctor. Then, remain in bed, lying very still and quiet until he is able to assure you that the danger of losing baby has passed.

It is not easy, I know, to go to bed in these busy

times but a few days inconvenience, however trying, is far better than the enforced rest a miscarriage would entail, to say nothing of the bitter disappointment of losing a much-wanted little one.

On being allowed to get up and about again, take things extra quietly, avoid long journeys and heavy housework and try to rest in bed (or to sit with your feet up) for the few days when the periods would normally be due for the next two successive months.

Forewarned is Forearmed

Certainly the last thing you want to do is to be constantly looking out for upsets. But at the same time it is sensible and wise to know that bad or persistent sickness in the early months and sickness of any kind during the later months, bad headaches, dizziness, swellings of the hands, face, legs or feet, persistent sleeplessness, heavy tired feelings, great thirst, marked despondency, severe backache, abdominal cramp and any losses or discharges (other than a slight colourless secretion from the vagina) may be signs warning you that all is not as it should be. Forewarned here is forearmed.

If you know what symptoms are not normal, you will know also that should you notice any one of them yourself, the thing to do is to pay an immediate visit to your doctor or midwife so that they can diagnose any impending trouble, and tell you what to do to check it before it has had time to get a real start.

The nine months of pregnancy should be happy ones. You should be feeling well and looking forward with eagerness to the arrival of your baby, and your medical advisers should be well satisfied with your progress.

Last Two Months

During the last two months of your pregnancy, your doctor or nurse will probably ask to see you more often. A baby grows a great deal during that time and those who are looking after you like to make sure that the child continues to lie in the best position for the birth. They will also want to take your blood pressure and test your water more frequently. So arrange for these extra visits, knowing that they are for your own good and for the good of your unborn baby.

Relaxation

The ability to relax completely at will or when asked to do so by your doctor or nurse during your confinement is a big help towards natural childbirth, so if your ante-natal clinic holds relaxation classes, attend these regularly. Where there are no such classes held in your area, booklets on relaxation are obtainable from many book shops now.

Baby's Birth

Labour is divided into three stages. The unborn baby normally lies head pointing downwards, in a bag of fluid. During the first stage of labour the muscle fibres forming the mouth of the womb dilate, while those forming the body of the womb contract. Each contraction forces the liquid in the bag to bulge through the mouth of the womb so opening it wider and wider. Soon the pressure will cause the bag to burst, and you will feel a gush of fluid which mothers often call the " breaking of the waters."

When the mouth of the womb is wide open, so that baby's head and body can pass through it easily, the second stage of labour begins. The contractions now, as each one comes on, make you want to bear down and push, because they are actually forcing baby out of the womb and along the birth canal. The second stage ends with the arrival of your own little child in the world.

The third stage is very short. It just consists of the expulsion of the afterbirth, about twenty minutes later.

CHAPTER VI

NEW MOTHER AND BABY

WITH your baby now lying safely at your side, your mother-instinct will surge forward so quickly that outside events will, for the time being, tend to sink right into the background, and for the ten to fourteen days that you will be in bed (or at any rate in your room) you will be delightfully free to enjoy your little one, the visits of your husband and the congratulations of your friends.   You will be free, also, to learn much that may be new to you now that you are a mother ; free to devote a certain amount of time each day to getting your figure back to normal ; free to lay the early paving-stones for successful breast-feeding and to initiate baby quietly and gently into his early routines.

Early Days

These days, the first of many to be filled with the joy and the gladness of motherhood, are immensely important ones both to you and to your child, and it certainly goes without saying that you will want to make the very best use of them you possibly can.

Visitors as a general rule are restricted at first, so apart from your husband and perhaps one or two near relations, you may be forbidden other callers for some days.   It is as well to make up your mind to this possibility beforehand, and to warn your friends too.   Then neither you nor they will be disappointed.

A new mother invariably feels very tired just at first, and although she picks up after she has had a few hours rest and a sound sleep, and becomes radiant in health and in happiness, looking and feeling extremely fit and well, we do find that both mother and child get on far better when they are kept quiet during the days immediately following the confinement.

The mother needs rest and peace no less than her little baby, to whom everything is very new and totally

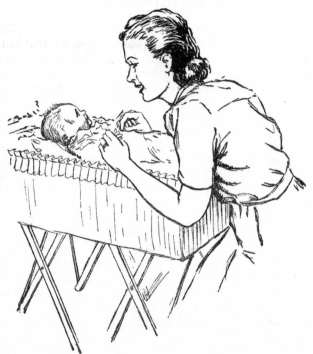

These days, the first of many to be filled with gladness.

different from his days in the darkness of the womb. Here in the world everything is light and bright ; voices echo in place of the complete silence ; forms move about where before all was so still; arms lift him up and put him down (Fig. 27). In a matter of moments baby has, in fact, become a very new member of a very large and a very busy community about which he knows nothing at all.

It will be some considerable time before your child begins to realise even a fraction of all this, because for a few weeks after his birth every infant lives in a partial continuation of his prenatal state. This accounts for

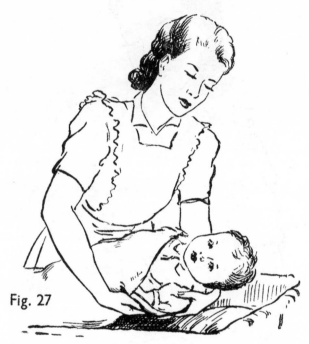

Fig. 27

the fact that the new-born baby sleeps away most of his time quite oblivious to his surroundings, and it explains why he only rouses himself for short intervals when he is being bathed and fed.

The more gradual is a baby's introduction to life in the world, therefore, the better. So for this reason, if for no other, modulate your voice when you talk to your little one. Quiet, soft tones will comfort and soothe him.

Fig 28

They will reassure him and as time goes on he will learn to love the sound of your voice and to listen for it.

When you take him in your arms hold him firmly. (Fig. 28). That gives him a sense of security and helps to dispel the fear that babies have of being dropped.

Remember that grown-ups can look like giants to a tiny child, so be careful not to peer too closely into his face. Try to shield your baby, too, from sudden very loud noises. They are always frightening and disturbing, and though babies do, and should, learn to sleep through the ordinary sounds of the household, and while it is both unwise and unnecessary to walk about on tiptoe or to speak in whispers because the baby is asleep, you always want to avoid startling a child.

Regaining Your Figure

Quite soon after baby's birth your figure will begin to return to normal. To assist the abdominal muscles to regain their form in the least possible time, exercise or else massage—often both—are becoming increasingly popular. Some doctors like their patients to start on a few exercises the day after the baby's birth, others prefer them to wait until two or more days have elapsed. Your doctor or nurse will know what is best for you.

Exercises are always more interesting when they are done to music. Wireless tunes in rather slow dance-band rhythms suit these exercises admirably. Keep the movements well timed, and relax for a few minutes between each exercise.

The exercises illustrated and described on Chart 3 are some of the best for the new mother. They are done in bed with the pillows removed and the upper bed clothes turned well back, or removed, to allow ample freedom. If you like you can wear a dressing gown, though on warm days this will not be necessary. Remember to keep the knees slightly flexed, that is, drawn up about three inches off the mattress, and keep the heels pressed firmly down.

CHART 3
EXERCISES FOR THE NEW MOTHER

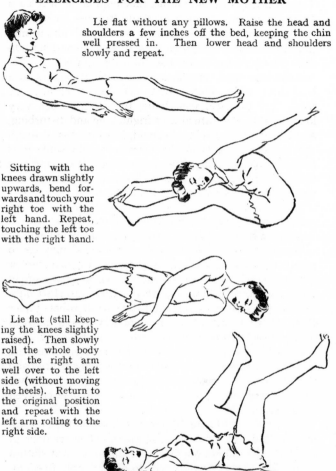

Lie flat without any pillows. Raise the head and shoulders a few inches off the bed, keeping the chin well pressed in. Then lower head and shoulders slowly and repeat.

Sitting with the knees drawn slightly upwards, bend forwards and touch your right toe with the left hand. Repeat, touching the left toe with the right hand.

Lie flat (still keeping the knees slightly raised). Then slowly roll the whole body and the right arm well over to the left side (without moving the heels). Return to the original position and repeat with the left arm rolling to the right side.

Lie flat. Dig the small of your back well into the bed, raise both legs high into the air, and pretend to pedal a huge bicycle.

Besides these set exercises you should make a point of lying prone, flat on your abdomen, for twenty minutes twice a day. This helps to drain the womb, and it also greatly assists it to return to a good position internally. You can do your abdominal lying at any time convenient, but the best time for your exercises is in the morning.

The New Mother's Day

With the exception of some exercises, periods of abdominal lying (that is lying prone, face downwards), and a rest in the afternoon, the new mother generally spends the day sitting well propped in bed. This makes letter writing, reading, knitting and sewing all very easy and delightful occupations.

The length of time you have to stay in bed will vary, according to your own needs and the opinion of your doctor. Some new mothers get up much sooner than others.

Make the most of the time your nurse is looking after you. Ask to be allowed to change baby on several occasions so that when you are on your own you will feel perfectly at home doing this. Once you are up, she will let you help in the bathing of your little one.

Ask your nurse to show you exactly how to hold baby out. It is much too soon yet to begin habit training in earnest, but you can introduce holding baby over his pot while he is young in the hope of catching him at convenient times, provided this is not taken too seriously. It is a great mistake to over-train a child. It only leads to lapses later on which can be very disappointing to an earnest young mother. It is far better to delay real training until he is older and even then, not to expect too much.

When holding baby out, be careful not to do so for longer than two minutes at the outside, and if nothing happens, never mind. When it does, a little gentle praise, adopting the attitude that baby has done what was expected of him, is helpful.

The correct position is important. You should sit on

Fig 29

a comfortable, low chair with the receptacle grasped between your thighs, baby's back resting against your front, and both your hands free to hold the lower part of his buttocks and the upper parts of his legs down to the knees (Fig. 29). The pot or chamber need not be warmed unless your baby shows a marked dislike to a cool one. The cold rim pressing lightly against his body helps to suggest to him what is required, and, as time goes on, he will learn to respond more and more easily.

Baby's Sleep

Like all young creatures, babies need plenty of sleep. During the first few weeks of his life, yours should spend most of his time sleeping, and except for when he is being bathed and dressed, and the time spent over his feeds, he should have very few wakeful moments. Up to the age of about four months, at least twenty hours' sleep out of the twenty-four should be the rule. From four to seven months old, eighteen hours will suffice, and from seven months old to a year, seventeen hours.

Most babies wake in the night at first, and this is likely to happen to yours too. But, as time goes on, baby will learn to sleep the night through. If he does not, and you are sure he is not hungry (one of the chief reasons for an infant waking in the early hours) then it may be that he is uncomfortable. He may be too warm or he may be too cold, or his feet alone may be chilly. He may be lying on a crease in the lower blanket. He may have an attack of wind, and this will cause spasms of pain that are bound to wake him up.

Or, he may be suffering from red or sore buttocks. These would smart terribly each time he passed water or a wet part of his napkin touched his skin and would be quite enough to waken him up.

Baby's Cot

Baby's cot may be made of wicker, canvas or wood.

It should be provided with a stand to keep it off the floor where there is always a draught.

The inside should be lined with washable material such as calico or sateen. The outside may be draped in any way you fancy, but except for a few folds of material to form the top head drapings, curtains and canopies should be avoided. They exclude the air, and baby needs as much fresh air as possible (Fig. 7).

The requirements for the cot are quite simple. They consist of :

    1 hair or flock mattress
    1 mackintosh sheet to cover this
    1 under blanket
    1 large or two small top cot blankets
    1 eiderdown and coverlet if wished
    1 small flat pillow (not made of feathers) for later on
    1 hot-water bottle with a good cover

There are two ways of making up a baby's cot according to whether you have one large top cot blanket or two small ones.

If you are going to use the large blanket you open this out, remove the cot mattress and place the blanket in position across the cot with its top and bottom edges lying over the sides (Fig. 30). One side edge of the blanket should lie on a level with baby's chin. Over the blanket place the mattress, the mackintosh, and the under-blanket, in that order. Then bring one long end of the large blanket over and tuck it in on the other side. Do the same with the other long end. Finally turn up or turn under the bottom. This forms a very cosy envelope form of bed for baby (Fig. 31). It saves getting small cot blankets which would be too small for use later on in the larger sized cot every baby needs at toddler age.

The other way is to place a small mackintosh over the mattress, and cover this with the bottom blanket. Then place the two small cot blankets over this in the ordinary way and tuck them in at the bottom and sides.

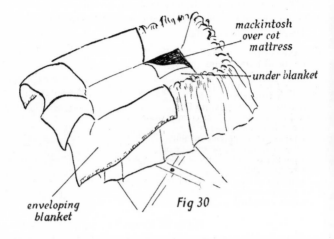

mackintosh
over cot
mattress

under blanket

enveloping
blanket

Fig 30

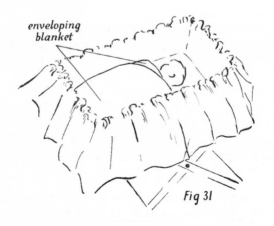

enveloping
blanket

Fig 31

Baby's Basket

Baby's basket, which may be lined to match the colour scheme of the cot, should have a well-fitting lid.

Inside the basket place:

1 cake of baby soap
1 tube of baby cream
1 tin of baby powder
   or { 1 oz. starch powder } in their original packets
       { 1 oz. zinc powder }
A 2 oz. packet of white lint
A 4 oz. packet of best cotton wool
1 bottle of baby lotion
1 jar of white petroleum jelly
   or 2 oz. of olive or similar oil
1 packet of large rustless safety pins
1 reel of white cotton
1 needle of size suitable for the cotton
1 pair of round ended scissors
1 soft hairbrush

Baby's Pram

Very small prams are not really economical. A child so soon outgrows them. Very deep prams are not to be recommended either, because the baby does not get enough fresh air. Prams that are pushed from behind should be avoided too, otherwise a mother is constantly pushing her baby against the cold wind.

The ideal pram is on the large side, the handle is in front, there is a safety strap (for use later on), a good wheel brake, a hood and mackintosh cover for wet days, and a sun canopy for summer.

Baby's Bath

Many mothers do not worry about getting a special bath for the baby. They use the grown-ups' bath from the beginning. If you get a small one, then a plastic or papier-mâché bath is best. Two bath towels and a little chamber should also be provided. A small screen and a clothes horse will also prove invaluable.

Baby's bath should be a source of delight both to him and to you. Up to the age of about six to eight months old, the usual plan is for the bath to take place in the morning at about 9.30 a.m.   In the evening he is washed but not bathed.   There is, though, no reason at all why you should not reverse the times and give the bath at 5.30 p.m. and the smaller wash in the mornings.

Whichever time you do choose, though, the same care will be needed, particularly at first, to see that baby is in no way startled or frightened when he is put into the water.   For this reason, always lower him gently (Fig. 32).

Be careful to see that the water is the right temperature, neither too hot nor too cold.   It should register 100° F. at first, but as he grows older, provided he is healthy and well and it agrees with him, you can gradually reduce the temperature, starting when he is about two months old, so that by the time he is six months old the water is 80° F.   Test the heat with a bath thermometer if you have one.   If not, you can judge it with the tip of your bare elbow.   When the water feels just comfortable to your naked flesh, the temperature is about 100° F.

Before commencing the bath, make sure that you have everything to hand, and at the last moment wash your hands thoroughly.

The following is a list of the things you will require:

Bath
Bath thermometer
Hot and cold water
Soap
Lint, face cloth or square of butter muslin for the face
Similar of larger size for washing the body
Cotton-wool swabs and some warm boiled water
Baby powder
Two warmed towels
Pail to receive soiled napkins
Basket to receive clothes taken off
Clean napkins and a set of clothes warming at the fire
Hairbrush
Large flannel apron
Scales
Screen to protect baby from draughts
Fireguard before the fire
Small table covered with a blanket on which to lay baby *or*
A low chair to sit on in which case baby lies on your knee

Fill the bath to a depth of about five inches, putting the cold water in first and then the hot. Stir the water round to distribute the heat evenly and have both hot and cold water handy to bring the temperature up to 100° F. by the time you are ready to begin.

Nearby have two small bowls (one rather larger than the other, into which you have poured some luke warm, previously boiled, water. Place baby's face cloth in the larger bowl and a few cotton wool swabs, the size of damsons, in the smaller bowl.

Having washed your hands first and put on the flannel apron, undress baby as far as his vest either on the table on a blanket or on your knee. Wring out a swab in the boiled water and attend to baby's nose with it. Wipe downwards on the outside first, and then with another swab, gently swab round the nostrils. On no account should twists of wool be pushed up the nose. If baby, sneezes, so much the better. It is to be hoped that he will. Nothing cleanses the nose more thoroughly. No attempt should be made to clean the eyes or the mouth. Tears and the natural flow of saliva are quite sufficient cleansing agents on their own, we consider in these days. Next wash and dry the rest of the face and the ears with the warm boiled water.

Remove baby's vest and napkin and wrap him in a warm towel while you attend to his head toilet. Re-test the heat of the water, adjust it if necessary and then begin to wash the hair very gently. Once a week you can do so with soap, but on the other days you should use plain warm water. Rinse well over the bath and then dry both head and hair thoroughly.

Loosen the folds of the towel, soap both your hands, work up a good lather and pass them lightly over his body and limbs, always working upwards and towards his heart. When he has been soaped, he is ready to be slowly and gently lowered into the warm water (Fig. 32). With your left hand and arm support his neck and

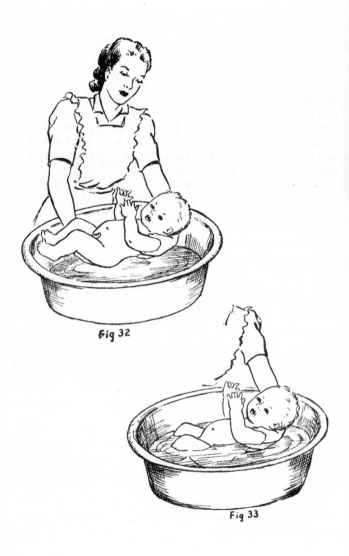

Fig 32

Fig 33

shoulders, grasping his left shoulder with your fingers. With your right hand hold him under the buttocks. When he is safely in the bath, free your right hand and use it to splash a little water over him. Hold baby securely while you do so with your left hand (Fig. 33), and let him have a few moments of kicking and splashing on his own. Then turn him over and splash his back and finally lift him out on to a towel. With the second towel, dry him carefully. When he is quite dry (be extra careful of the creases round the neck, under the arms, in the groins and the fold of the buttocks) give his body a light dusting with powder and put on his vest.

Baby can then be held out in the hope that he may pass water and have a motion. When he has finished, wash and powder those parts again. If, by any chance, there is any reddening of the skin you can use a little baby cream instead of the powder. Put on his clean napkins and finish dressing him.

Dressing Baby

It is best to clothe your baby according to the weather. During the early months boys and girls are dressed alike, vest and napkins coming first. There are two ways of putting on baby's napkin. I prefer the method that uses the napkin as an oblong instead of a triangle. Fold the napkin long ways, place one narrow end under baby's buttocks, draw the other through the legs (Fig. 34), turn in any superfluous (to give added protection where it is most needed) and fasten with safety-pins on each hip.

The next garments consist of the day-nightgown and bootees; or a petticoat, gown and bootees; or a knitted jersey and long knitted pull-ups. As these last have feet attached, bootees are not necessary. In any of these three cases baby can wear a matinée coat in the house on cold days and in the early morning and after tea. As he grows older he will wear a pram set out of doors in cool and cold weather.

D*

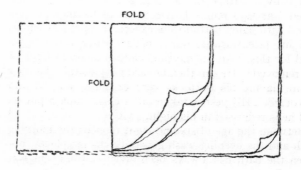

FOLD

FOLD

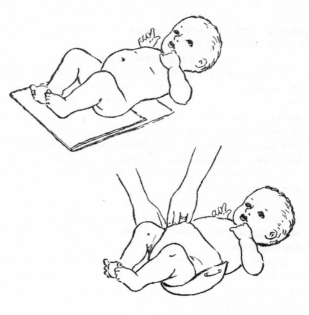

Fig. 34

Evening Time

If baby is bathed in the morning, he is " topped and tailed " at 5.30 p.m. This consists of having his nose wiped with damp cotton wool exactly as in the mornings and his face washed, warm boiled water being again used for this. All his daytime clothes down to his vest are removed. He can then be held out over his chamber before having his buttocks very carefully washed and powdered. His vest is taken off, a clean napkin put on and he is redressed in his nightgown.

Between the age of six and eight months the morning bath and the evening wash generally change places, but when the bath has always been given in the evening it naturally continues.

The evening bath should be kept up throughout child-hood. The morning wash can be modified by gradual degrees as your child grows until it consists of a quick all-over wash followed by a rapid, cold sponge-down and a good rub with a rough bath towel.

Baby's Exercise

All young creatures need exercise and your baby will be no exception to this rule. Right from the first there should be complete freedom of movement for every muscle of his body. That is one reason why his clothes should be loose and light, and why, too, no binder is necessary once the navel has healed, and the bandage that held the dressing in place has been discarded.

In addition to the exercise baby will take on his own accord, the medical profession is becoming more and more emphatic as to the value of a few specified exercises planned on the most simple lines for babies from the age of about two months old. These help a child to develop good posture.

At first, each exercise should last for less than a minute, but as time goes on baby can continue for about six minutes in all. On charts Nos. 4, 5, 6 and 7 you will find these illustrated and described.

Sun and Air Baths

From quite an early age you can give your baby sun and air baths. In fine weather he can take these out of doors. Lay a blanket or mattress on the ground and let baby lie naked on this. Start with a short exposure and gradually increase the time each day.

Early in the morning and again towards teatime are the ideal times for sun and air bathing, for the ultra violet rays are then at their best and yet the sun is not too hot. It does not matter if the sun is not shining, the health-giving rays come through fine cloud, but, in the height of summer it is best to give baby his open air bath under a shady tree. If you have no garden, there may be a park nearby. Failing this and if you have not got a balcony you will have to let baby lie before an open window. It is useless giving him a sunbath with the window closed because the beneficial rays cannot penetrate ordinary glass. When the sun is out baby's head, eyes and neck should be shaded from the glare.

Weights and Gains

While some babies are heavier and some lighter than others, the average weight at birth is round about 7 lbs. A healthy child is neither too fat nor too thin. His muscles are firm and his skin is clear. At first it will be pale pink; as time goes on it should become a healthy tan.

During the first four or five days of life most babies lose anything up to half a pound or so. After that they should begin to gain, and should continue to do so at a steady rate, adding about five to seven ounces to their weight each week up to six months old, and roughly a pound a month from six months to a year.

Signs of Good Health

During the first few days of life, the motions passed by a baby are of a blackish colour. These are known as meconium stools. Once this meconium has passed out

CHART 4
BABY'S EXERCISES
from 2 to 3 Months Old

Baby lies on his back (on your knee) clad in a vest only. He is encouraged to fight out with his arms and legs as vigorously as he will. Just before or after the morning bath and again after tea are two of the best times.

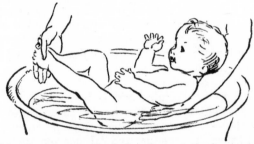

This takes place in the bath. Support the head, neck and shoulders and back along the length of your left forearm and hand, and grasp his feet with your right hand. Gently swish him forwards and backwards in the water. Baby's arms should be free and move at will.

Lying face downwards on your knee (clad only in his vest) encourage baby to lift his head and look round. This exercise is excellent for strengthening the back muscles.

CHART 5
BABY'S EXERCISES
from 3 to 6 Months Old

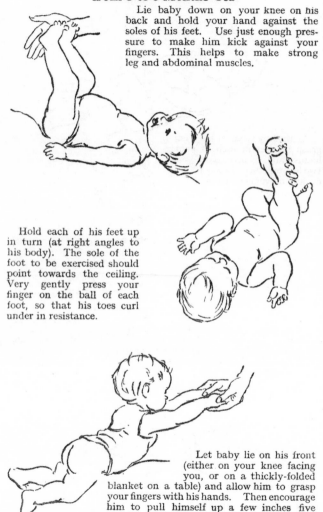

Lie baby down on your knee on his back and hold your hand against the soles of his feet. Use just enough pressure to make him kick against your fingers. This helps to make strong leg and abdominal muscles.

Hold each of his feet up in turn (at right angles to his body). The sole of the foot to be exercised should point towards the ceiling. Very gently press your finger on the ball of each foot, so that his toes curl under in resistance.

Let baby lie on his front (either on your knee facing you, or on a thickly-folded blanket on a table) and allow him to grasp your fingers with his hands. Then encourage him to pull himself up a few inches five or six times. This exercise strengthens neck, back and chest muscles.

CHART 6
BABY'S EXERCISES
from 6 to 9 Months Old

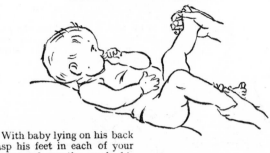

With baby lying on his back grasp his feet in each of your hands and gently work his two legs together to make pedal-cycling movements in the air.

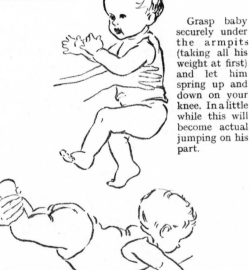

Grasp baby securely under the armpits (taking all his weight at first) and let him spring up and down on your knee. In a little while this will become actual jumping on his part.

Turn baby on his face, take his ankles in one hand, and with the other firmly support his chest and body. Attract his attention from above so that curiosity forces him to lift his head and arch his back.

CHART 7
BABY'S EXERCISES
from 9 to 12 Months Old

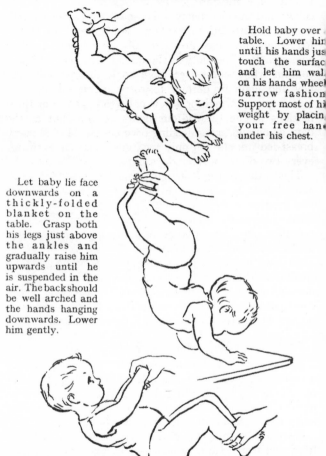

Hold baby over a table. Lower him until his hands just touch the surface and let him walk on his hands wheelbarrow fashion. Support most of his weight by placing your free hand under his chest.

Let baby lie face downwards on a thickly-folded blanket on the table. Grasp both his legs just above the ankles and gradually raise him upwards until he is suspended in the air. The back should be well arched and the hands hanging downwards. Lower him gently.

Baby lies on the table, you grasp his ankles with one hand and his wrists with the other. Then steady his feet and let him pull himself up to sitting position. As he grows older, add another movement to this exercise. Let him pull himself from a sitting to a standing position, while you steady him with your hands at his wrists and feet.

of the system, however, the stools should resemble freshly-made mustard, or freshly scrambled egg both in colour and in consistency. Those of a breast-fed infant are of a slightly brighter yellow than those of the bottle-fed child and they are generally of a more curdled consistency. The motions should not, as a general thing, contain white curds (see page 204), though odd ones now and again are nothing to worry about.

It is quite normal for a new baby to pass two or three motions in the twenty-four hours at first, but as the days go on and breast feeding becomes established many breast-fed infants will only pass one a day or even one every two or every three days.

This is due to the fact that human milk is very easily assimilated; it contains little waste. It is very important that a mother understands this fact because so many (especially with their first babies) mistake the condition for constipation and start giving opening medicines, which is quite wrong.

So long as the child is obviously thriving, gaining steadily, sleeping well, is happy and bright and the motions when they are passed are normal, this is not constipation at all and no treatment or medicine is needed while breast milk remains the staple food.

Why Does Baby Cry ?

All babies cry a certain amount but there is generally a very good reason for it when baby is constantly fretful or cries a lot. It is often difficult, though, for a new mother to distinguish between the different causes for tears, and to know why her baby is so sad.

He may be hungry, or thirsty, or cold or suffering from cold feet. He may have wind, colic, earache, jaw-ache, or some other pain or discomfort, including that of sore or red buttocks which might cause bad smarting each time he passes urine.

Baby may cry when he has been very sick, when he

gets over-hot, when he is lying on a crease or when he wants to be turned over, when his hot bottle is too warm or too near to him.   He may cry when he is frightened, or angered through being disturbed by some sudden or unexpected loud noise ; when he is badly constipated ; when he is teething or not well.   He will cry too when he wants to be played with, or amused and, as he gets older, when his activities are restricted or when he meets strangers, or his mother goes out of his sight.

Under the age of six months, perhaps, two of the most common reasons for crying are hunger as the result of under-feeding (the food being either insufficient in quantity or poor in quality or both), and failure to bring up wind during and after each feed.   In a baby who is gaining heavily, crying may be due to discomfort set up by over-feeding also, but this is not so common.

If the gains are under five to seven ounces weekly the remedy lies in increasing the quantity or improving the quality of the feeds, or both.

Where wind is the trouble, hold baby up against your shoulder (Fig. 37) and gently pat his back until the wind has been expelled.   If this does not relieve him, a hot fomentation placed over the abdomen probably will, especially if you give him a teaspoonful of plain dill water in the same amount of plain warm boiled water.

CHART 8
BABY'S PROGRESS

In this chart there are three columns.   The first sets out the progressive landmarks.   The second gives the average age at which each is reached as a guide.   The third is left blank so that you can fill in your own baby's records.   Remember that individual babies vary very greatly in their accomplishments ; some talk before they walk, others walk before they talk.   Most have eight teeth at a year, some less, a few more.   Only if your baby is seriously behind need you worry.

Baby's Progress	Average Age	Baby's Record
Begins to stare at a window	1 month old	....
Seems interested in faces	2 months old	....
Stops to listen to voices and music	2 months old	....
Follows mother with his eyes ..	2 months old	....
Plays with his fingers	3 months old	....
Smiles at mother's approach ..	3 months old	....
Laughs out aloud	4 months old	....
Will help himself when lifted ..	4 months old	....
Tries to sit up ..	4 months old	....
Enjoys a rattle ..	5 months old	....
Shows annoyance at being thwarted	5 months old	....
Cuts the first lower tooth	6 months old	....
Plays with his toes	6 months old	....
Is shy with strangers	6 months old	....
Can beat on the table	7 months old	....
Will look for a toy	7 months old	....
Calls out Dad-Dad	7 months old	....
Cuts the first upper tooth ..	8 months old	....
Claps his hands ..	8 months old	....
Begins to crawl ..	9 months old	....
Waves good-bye	9 months old	....
Stands alone ..	12 months old	....
Possesses eight teeth	12 months old	....
Takes a few steps alone	15 months old	....
Begins to use a spoon	15 months old	....
Can say four words	15 months old	....
Forms the first sentence ..	18 months old	....
Climbs on to a low chair	18 months old	....
Can point out his nose	18 months old	....

You will know by examination whether he is cold or too hot, wet, or lying on a crease, or whether his hot water bottle is as it should be. His willingness or otherwise to drink a little warm boiled water from a teaspoon will tell you whether he is thirsty. You will notice if the skin on his buttocks is sore or even red, while the passing of hard or formed motions will indicate to you that he is constipated. The fact that baby is ready to laugh and play or be comforted the moment you go to pick him up, will let you know that he is tired of being on his own, and that he may need your company.

Earache is more difficult to discern, but when a child frequently rolls his head or keeps putting his hand up to his ear and crying at the same time, you can always suspect pain in that region, while any discharge from the ears almost certainly confirms this. Always consult a doctor where there is ear trouble, however slight.

Jawache is generally associated with teething. It is probably not very common at so early an age, but it may be shown by baby's disinclination for hard crusts, in addition to crying.

The hunger cry is loud and determined. You will quickly learn to recognise it because it ceases immediately food is given.

The cry of bad pain is very loud and distressed. It may even be a scream. It is true that it may diminish a little if baby is picked up and nursed, but it will not cease until the pain goes. When the pain is due to wind, the legs are generally drawn tightly upwards and the abdomen may feel hard.

Pain caused by teething, earache, feverishness and the onset of illness is generally more of a whimpering nature, but always where you are not able to pacify him easily by simple means, or where the pain or crying is persistent or baby appears poorly, or is very pale, or feverish, or shows difficulty in passing urine, or has diarrhoea, consult your doctor at once and do not attempt anything on your own.

Teething Time

Although the first set or the milk teeth are already in the jaws at birth, they do not, as a rule, begin to come through the gums until a child is about six months old.

The exact age at which the first tooth is cut is liable to vary a little, but the following table gives the order in which they generally appear.

Customary Age		Teeth due to appear
6th to 7th months	..	2 Lower centre front teeth
8th to 9th months	..	4 Upper centre teeth
10th to 12th months	..	2 Lower teeth, one on each side of the centre ones
12th to 16th months	..	4 Back teeth or Molars
18th to 20th months	..	4 Canine or Eye teeth (two upper and two lower)
2 to 2½ years ..	..	4 Big back teeth or Back Molars

Provided a child is healthy and has been correctly looked after and correctly fed, teething should produce very few upsets, though some babies, it is true, do tend to suffer more than others.

There is, however, a lot you can do to make teething easier. First of all it is important to keep baby's clothes extra dry from the dribbling. If necessary, put a rubber bib underneath his ordinary one, or under his gown or jersey. Sodden dresses and bibs, tend to chill a child and this encourages cutting the teeth with bronchitis.

Next, you can put your baby to sleep on alternate sides and not on his back. This helps the additional saliva to run out of his mouth, rather than trickle back into the throat, where it may be inclined to set up irritation and chestiness. Give him a bone-ring as early as you like, within reason, and encourage him to bite on that because it brings blood to the gums, and that encourages good teeth to develop beneath their surface. Rusks and crusts do the same. They should be given dry and hard; not be soaked in milk, or crushed up with his dinner.

In the few cases where, owing to tenderness of the gums, he refuses to bite on anything really hard, some

Baby's teeth at about
6–7 months old.

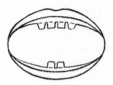

At about 8–9 months
old.

At about 10–12 months
old.

At about 12–16 months
old.

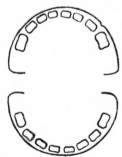

At about 18–20 months
old.

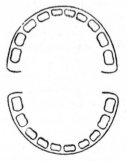

At about 2–2½ years
old.

well-washed raisins tied up in a perfectly clean and freshly laundered muslin bag, provides an excellent and soothing substitute. It has just the right resistance for tender little gums and the juice that baby will obtain from the raisins will be good for him too.

Frequent sips of cool boiled water are very soothing to a mouth that is hot and tender, or alternatively, drinks of comfortably warm water will often bring relief.

Always remember that a little extra mothering is a big help at teething time, that food which is unwanted should never be forced (particularly if baby seems hot or feverish) and that soothing medicines and powders should only be given on a doctor's orders. An occasional dose of fluid magnesia will help to cool the blood and regulate the bowels, if there is any tendency towards constipation, but, if baby appears to be in pain or if you think he is suffering from earache (indicated by his putting his hands up to one or both ears frequently and crying at the same time), you would be wise to let your doctor see him.

As soon as the first teeth are well down through the gums, they may be very gently brushed with an up-and-down movement once a day, using a small very soft toothbrush. Any good dental paste or some precipitated chalk may be used. Once a week a little plain salt, and once a week plain bicarbonate of soda can take the place of the usual dentifrice. When eight to ten teeth are completely through they may be cleaned twice a day, and from the age of eighteen months, give a slice of apple or similar tooth-cleansing food after each meal.

Vaccination

You would be wise to have baby vaccinated against smallpox, for although we seldom have epidemics of this very serious illness in our country now-a-days, there is always the chance that an outbreak may occur through the complaint being brought by a traveller from overseas.

Your doctor will advise you about this, and also suggest

the best time for it to be done. Some mothers and doctors like to get this over before the maternity nurse leaves the mother. Sometimes it is done when the mother has her post-natal check-up six weeks after her confinement. Sometimes baby is vaccinated later. In babyhood vaccination is a very simple matter with no known ill effects. It only leaves one small scar on the arm or leg, but a child should be in good health at the time of vaccination.

Immunisation

Immunisation is your baby's surest safeguard against the ravages of diphtheria. Your doctor will advise you as to the best time to have this done. It consists, merely, of two pricks at monthly intervals in the arm or buttock. As baby can also be protected against whooping cough by immunisation, your doctor may give a combined whooping cough and diphtheria immunisation at the same time.

Immunisation against an illness is not an absolute guarantee that your child cannot contract it, but it does protect the majority of children in a wonderful way. If an immunised child should fall a victim, the attack should be far less severe than it would otherwise have been. Moreover, the risk of complications (such as heart failure, bronchial pneumonia and paralysis, which are so prone to follow diphtheria) is practically removed.

Your Own Health

By the time baby is six weeks old the period-like loss which generally lasts for ten days after a confinement, but may dwindle for rather longer, should have cleared up. You should be feeling well, fit and strong.

Now is the time to pay one final visit to your doctor or midwife so that they can make an internal examination and satisfy themselves that the womb has returned to its normal position and size. This is very important because if it has not, it is an easy matter to put it right at this stage, whereas if neglected and left, it will probably give you a good deal of backache and discomfort later. In bad cases, it may even mean surgical treatment at some future date where now a bottle of medicine, some exercises or simple manipulation is all that would be required.

Birth Control

Provided the confinement has been normal, it is wise and usual to refrain from intercourse during the first four to six weeks after baby's birth. Conception during the post-natal months is not impossible whether the periods are present or not, and breast-feeding is no guarantee against it. It is less likely, though, to occur if the periods are absent, and also during the first eight to twelve weeks of the baby's life.

If you desire to space your family it is always much wiser to seek specialised advice on the subject rather than to refrain from intercourse (unless on religious grounds), occupy separate rooms or rely upon the withdrawal method called " being careful," which is not only very trying to the nerves of both husband and wife— particularly the wife—and by no means always reliable.

Most doctors will give instruction on birth control (the prevention of conception) if they are asked to do so, or the information may be obtained from practically all Welfare Centres and every Birth Control Clinic.

Follow-up Exercises

A little later on you may find it very useful to know of a few follow-up exercises specially designed to help remove superfluous flesh in the region of the waist (popularly known as a " spare tyre ") and correct a protruding abdomen, if either should be present from a previous confinement or even left behind for some reason or other from this one.

There is no point in starting follow-up exercises too soon, but if by the time you have weaned your baby,

CHART 9
FOLLOW-UP EXERCISES

Sit on the bed with the legs apart and the knees quite straight. Then using a series of little jerks try to touch the toes with first the right hand and then the left.

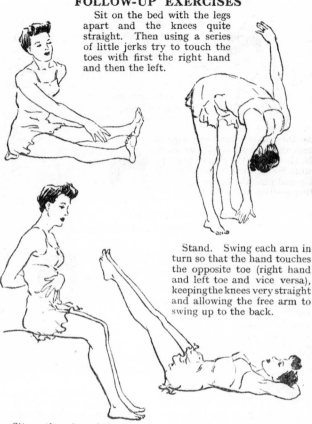

Stand. Swing each arm in turn so that the hand touches the opposite toe (right hand and left toe and vice versa), keeping the knees very straight and allowing the free arm to swing up to the back.

Sit on the edge of the bed, with the knees pressed together, head up and shoulders well back. Place the left hand on the protruding abdomen and the right hand on the small of the back. Count three and draw in the abdominal muscles as far as possible. Then relax and change hands.

Lie flat on the bed, placing the hands well behind the neck. Straighten the knees and then, keeping the legs and feet closely touching, breathe in and raise the feet as high as you comfortably can. Lower the legs and feet, breathing out at the same time.

CHART 10
EXERCISES FOR THE BUST

Cross the hands back to back and place them on top of the head. Without moving the hands, stretch the arms upwards exerting firm pressure on the back of each hand as you do so.

asp the hands behind the nape of neck and drop the head downwards the chest with the elbows pointing wards. Swing the elbows to the side skly and raise the head. Return to rting position and repeat.

Stretch the arms out at shoulder level with the palms facing downwards. Slowly rotate the hands until the palms face upwards. Return to the starting position and repeat.

Clinch the fists tightly and place them at the sides of and as near to the armpits as you can. Then make large circles in the air with the elbows.

Lie face downwards with the elbows bent and the palms of the hands under the chest. Straighten the arms at the same time raising the trunk and head. Then lower again to the starting position. Be careful when doing this exercise to keep the abdomen firmly held in. It must not be allowed to sag.

your abdomen or your figure is not as good as you would like, there are some exercises on Chart 9 which, if you persevere with them, should make appreciable difference in quite a short time.

Preserving the Bust

The golden rules for helping to preserve the contour of the bust are four:

1. Wear an uplifting brassiere during the carrying and the nursing months.
2. Wean slowly.
3. Tone up the breast muscles after weaning with the help of exercises.
4. Avoid worry, and if you have any womb trouble left from the confinement, have it attended to at once.

On Chart 10 you will find some exercises which are of great value in toning up the important muscles that largely control the contour of the bust, and as soon as weaning is over you can begin to follow them once a day.

In cases where the breasts have already lost their shape badly, though, these bust exercises may be performed twice or even three times each day. In addition, bathing the chest for a few minutes with alternately hot and cold water is often helpful.

Time and thought devoted to looking after your figure is well spent if it helps you to preserve its becoming, youthful line and enables you to feel that having a baby has added to, not taken from, your personal grace and charm.

CHAPTER VII

THE NURSING MOTHER

No food is quite so good for your own baby as your own milk. There are several reasons for this. Human milk is meant for the human child. It is blended to suit his precise needs. It comes to him at the correct temperature. And, because it never contacts outside germs (as may an artificial food, however carefully prepared) human milk is absolutely pure.

Moreover, it confers on a child an increased resistance to certain infectious illnesses to which the baby may be exposed during his early life.

There is another thing, lying in your arms close to your body where it is comfortable and warm and feeding from your breast, gives baby a sense of security and happiness and joy that only the breast-fed babies ever really know.

So, feed your baby yourself if you possibly can right up until the time he is ready to be weaned. If this is quite out of the question, then breast-feed for as long as you are able to, even if it is only for quite a short while, and when you do have to give it up try to breast-feed him at any rate first thing in the morning and last thing at night, just giving the bottle during the day.

The First Few Feeds

One of the first things you must do is to encourage baby to be a good feeder. Whether he develops into a steady and placid sucker, as opposed to a restless and fidgety one, depends to a very large extent on how you offer the breast at the beginning, during the days immediately following his birth.

The great thing to remember is to let him take his own time in starting to suck ; to allow him to feel his way slowly and gradually and at his own pace, and to bear in mind the fact that a baby is not born hungry, and that at first he will not be inclined to take very much from you because he has sufficient nourishment inside him to last with very little more, for a day or two.

Your little one will probably be placed to the breasts for the first time when he is a few hours old. Allow him to lie there with the nipple uncovered and held enticingly close to his face. In time instinct will surely begin to assert itself, and his lips will start to search around for food. Then the tiny mouth will discover the nipple and a moment later the first few sucks will be made.

Feeding Times

It is better not to be too strict about baby's feeding times. As a rule a full-time, healthy infant settles down to four hourly feeds (at 6 a.m., 10 a.m., 2 p.m., 6 p.m. and 10 p.m.) by the time he is a few weeks old, though to start with he may be quite irregular and thrive better and be happier, too, on what we call demand feeding. This means giving the feeds as and when baby cries for them quite irrespective of the clock for he, of course, has no idea of time. He only knows when he is hungry, cold, lonely or in pain. A lot of crying not only gives him wind but is very frustrating to him and worrying to his mother. Practically all babies need a feed in the night at first, but most give this up on their own when about 2 months old and sleep right through from 10 p.m. to 6 a.m.

Each feed usually lasts fifteen to twenty minutes but baby may take all he needs in less time. Try to start each new feed with the breast at which he last left off.

Feeding Technique

Always wash your hands before feeding baby, and

both before and after each feed carefully cleanse each nipple with some perfectly clean cotton-wool wrung out of boiled water.

It is important to make sure that your baby is really comfortably cradled in your arm when feeding. His own hands should be quite free to caress your breasts both while he is sucking and afterwards when he has

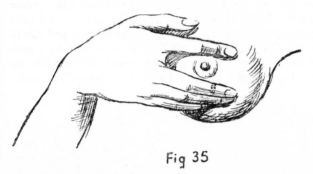

Fig 35

finished if he wants to. It is a great mistake to try and stop him or to secure his arms to his sides with a shawl.

Having settled baby comfortably, use your free hand to manipulate the breast. Hold it away from his nose. He needs complete freedom for breathing. If he cannot breathe freely he will relax his hold on the nipple, and show other signs of annoyance and vexation.

Learn to control the flow of the milk by placing your first and second fingers on the dark skin above and below the nipple, allowing the thumb to fall straight across the upper part of the breast (Fig. 35). By exerting just the right amount of pressure you will find you will soon be able to slow down the rate at which the milk will come through, and with practice you will acquire the knack of allowing it to flow at just the correct rate for your child's comfort and well-being.

When feeding you should see that baby gets a good

mouthful of breast, especially if the nipples are inclined
to be small, or not very good in shape (Fig. 36).   Sometimes it is a help to squeeze out a little milk immediately

Fig 36

before inserting each nipple into baby's mouth.

As the feeding breast empties, move your fingers a
little so that they support it from underneath.   This

will help baby to get the milk from the lower half, as well as the upper half. Make sure that he empties the first breast before changing over to the second one.

Be careful to guard against the breasts becoming engorged (too full) with milk. When this happens it is almost impossible for an infant to grip the nipple properly. His repeated efforts to get it far enough back into his mouth not only worry and tire him so that he fails to make a proper meal (and as a result is frequently termed lazy, which he is not), but they are liable to bruise the nipple skin. Cracks and sores may then appear.

If you find your breasts are uncomfortably full at feeding times, massage away some of the milk before putting baby to feed. This is easily done. The movement is the same one that you learnt when you were preparing your breasts during the carrying months. You slide the four fingers of each hand simultaneously down each side of each breast in turn, working the two thumbs down the front at the same time. Then bring thumbs and fingers towards one another as they approach the nipple. After two or three such movements you give the dark ring round the nipple a little squeeze and catch the milk in a glass (Figs. 24 and 25).

Right Atmosphere

Because the presence of others in the same room can be most disturbing to any but the youngest babe, try, whenever possible, and arrange to feed baby where it is quiet and where you two can be alone. When this cannot be managed then erect a screen around yourselves so that his attention is diverted as little as possible.

You will find it more comfortable if you sit on a low nursing chair when feeding baby (Fig. 8). If you are a busy mother and you tire easily, it is a good plan to recline on your bed and let baby lie by your side to take his feed.

Remember that a placid mother has more milk than one who is constantly worrying, so try to take life

E

calmly. Emotional disturbances are particularly liable
to interfere with the milk, so do your utmost to steer
clear of them. The happier you are and more care-free
your nature, the better nursing mother you will make.

Fig 37

Some breasts give up their milk very readily, particularly if the baby is a vigorous sucker. A number of
children, therefore, take all they need in a ten- or even
seven-minute feed instead of a twenty-minute one. There
is no harm in this, but when a baby does finish his feed
in less than twenty minutes the remainder of the time

should be devoted to allowing him to remain where he is, lying near to the breast that fed him because of the very deep psychological value he derives from such close proximity to his mother.

Fig 38

Bringing up Wind

All babies swallow a certain amount of air while feeding. And if they do not bring it up again, it may cause pains. You should not consider a feed complete until this swallowed air (or most of it) has been brought up before it has had time to pass from baby's stomach into his intestines and set up bouts of colic.

To keep baby comfortable and prevent colic and wind, hold him up against your shoulder half-way through and again at the end of each feed and firmly, but gently, pat the left side of his back, over the lower ribs until about two wind pops have escaped. Another method you can employ instead of holding baby to your shoulder is to sit him on your knee, support his back with one hand and his front with the other (Fig. 38), and sway him gently to and fro. The first method seems to suit one baby best ; the second another. Each are good, but for a mother with her first child, method number one is the more simple (Fig. 37).

Nursing Mother's Diet

Try to regulate your own diet now to suit your baby's needs and gains.

You may eat anything you fancy, with the exception of highly-seasoned dishes, vinegar, alcohol and unripe and over-ripe fruits. Amongst the best meats for you now are lamb, liver, beef, mutton, bacon, rabbit, fish, fowl and turkey. Of the fish, herrings, cod's roes and sprats are particularly valuable, though any fish on the market (with the exception of shellfish) is good.

All root vegetables are excellent and so are fresh salads and greens with special emphasis on spinach, cauliflower, turnip-tops, young stinging-nettle heads, peas, beans and brussels sprouts.

Fruit, fresh for preference, otherwise stewed, dried, bottled or canned, eggs (hens' not ducks'), custards, cheese, dried peas, haricot beans, boxed cereals, honey, margarine, butter, wholemeal and brown bread, chocolate and nuts (provided the latter are well chewed) all constitute a very valuable range of foods too.

The best liquids are milk, weak tea, weak coffee, meat extracts, lemonade, barley water, fruit juice and water, the juices from canned fruits with water added, cocoa, chocolate and gruel. Saccharine may be used, but sugar is preferable for sweetening.

The more fluid you drink, the more milk you will make.

Any kind of fluid will answer the purpose, but it is well to bear in mind that the richer it is, the richer your milk is likely to become, and this applies to foods in general.

If baby is not gaining enough despite the fact that you have plenty of milk, alter your own menu. Have cocoa in place of tea, make yourself some gruel and take this at night and again in the morning, have more dishes made from eggs and cheese. If you feel you are short of milk the thing to do is to drink more fluid. There should soon be an improvement, especially if you get extra rest as well, and avoid worrying about it.

Care of the Breasts

During the whole of the nursing period you should wear an uplifting brassière both day and night. The breasts are unusually heavy, and any downward drag will be very likely to result in the supporting skin being over-stretched. If this happens it causes a tendency to sagging after baby has been weaned and once that sagging has occurred it is very difficult to correct it.

Great care should be taken to keep the nipples scrupulously clean and completely free from stale and oozing milk. Nothing leads to cracks and sores more rapidly than stale milk which has been allowed to dry on the nipples. Both before and immediately after each feed, therefore, cleanse them carefully. Between feeds keep them covered with a square of linen that you have rendered germ-free by scorching it lightly.

At the very first sign of any soreness (should this occur in spite of your precautions) use a nipple shield on the affected side when feeding baby and paint the part with a little one-per-cent aluminium acetate or some Friar's balsam. This first remedy is particularly efficacious and is not nearly so well known as it might be. Its only disadvantage is momentary stinging, but it is so good that it is worth the temporary discomfort.

Any but the slightest soreness or cracking of the

nipples should be treated by your doctor and certainly if accompanied by any pain, swelling, tenderness or hardness of the breast itself.

Further Advice

Be careful what aperients you take now. Most will act on baby as well as on you. Cascara appears to upset babies least of them all, and for this reason it is one of the favourites for the nursing mother. Some mothers, though, find senna tea more satisfactory. Salts should be avoided, except when medically ordered.

There should be no reason why you should not smoke when you are not actually attending to your baby, provided you limit yourself to not more than four cigarettes a day and do not inhale. Heavy smoking is not good. After a certain time, nicotine is secreted by the milk.

Return of the Periods

There are no hard and fast rules about the nursing mother's periods. A few mothers will menstruate regularly during breast-feeding ; some only now and again ; others commence when their babies are six to seven months old, while many do not see anything until about six weeks after the child is completely weaned.

The appearance of the periods is no indication for early weaning and, as a rule, menstruation makes no difference either to the mother or her child. In the few cases where the milk diminishes slightly during those four or five days of the menstrual flow, small artificial feeds may be given to complement the breast, if the baby seems hungry, fretful or sad.

Fruit Juices and Vitamins

Each day from the age of one month baby needs fresh, or concentrated fruit juice, and a little cod- (or halibut-) liver oil. Commence with very small quantities and gradually increase. One quarter to one half teaspoonful of fresh, strained orange juice, diluted with the same amount of warm boiled water, is the right amount to give to a baby of one month, increasing to the strained juice of half an orange at six months old. If you are using the concentrated fruit juice, follow the directions on the bottle.

Cod-liver oil should be commenced in drop doses and worked up by degrees to the amounts stated on the bottle. Halibut-liver oil is given in drop doses all along. The amount is usually stated on the bottle.

CHAPTER VIII

ARTIFICIAL FEEDING

WITHOUT any doubt, breast milk is the ideal food for every baby and it is always better to breast feed if you possibly can. All the same, there are occasions when, for one reason or another, a child has to be brought up on an artificial food—either partially or wholly, as the case may be.

If for some good reason you have to put your baby on the bottle do not worry, but do try and restrict this to the daytime feeds and nurse him naturally yourself last thing at night and first thing in the morning if you possibly can. You will not deprive him entirely then of the comfort and the joy, as well as the many advantages breast feeding affords.

If You Must Bottle Feed

When you do give your baby a bottle feed, always remember that it is, at best, a substitute for a breast-feed. Let everything about it, therefore, resemble breast-feeding as closely as you can make it.

Sit on a low chair and hold baby cradled comfortably in the crook of your left arm. Cuddle him to you a little so that he may feel the warmth coming from your own body.

Make sure that the hole in the teat is the right size and the food the right temperature. To test the hole, turn the bottle upside down and notice how fast or how slowly the milk drips out. It should do so at the rate of one drop a second. If it drips slower than that you will have to enlarge the hole. This you do by sticking the eye end of a darning needle into a cork. Hold the

Fig 39

pointed end over a flame and when red-hot push the needle quickly through the hole in the teat. To test the heat hold the bottle up to your cheek or against the flesh of your bare forearm.

Giving the Bottle

While you are feeding baby keep a towel folded round the bottle to conserve the heat, and hold it at such an angle that the neck of the bottle is always full of milk otherwise baby will suck down air. Now and again during the feed, remove the bottle gently from baby's mouth and then replace it. Be careful to see that he does not gulp the food down. He should take fifteen to twenty minutes and suck steadily all the time.

Never leave a baby alone with a feeding bottle. Five things may happen and the last two can be very dangerous.

1. He may drop off to sleep and let the food get cold.
2. The neck may not be kept full of milk with the result that he will suck down air.
3. The bottle may fall out of his mouth altogether.
4. He may choke while you are not there.
5. He may be sick and, unable to get the teat out of his mouth, he may draw the milk back again into his lungs. This can be serious; even fatal.

Stay with baby while he feeds and hold the bottle yourself all the time, always.

Half-way through the feed and again at the end of it, help him to expel the wind exactly as a breast-fed child does (Figs. 37 and 38).

What to Give

You can feed baby on one of the dried baby milks on the market or you can use evaporated milk for him. In either case it is important to follow very closely the directions for mixing the feeds sold with whatever product you buy.

If you prefer to use liquid cows' milk and you can be

sure of your supply, you can make up your own milk mixture. Pasteurised cows' milk (Tuberculin Tested if possible) with the addition at first of water and sugar, is what we generally use.

During the first four days of life a bottle-fed baby should be fed according to your doctor's or midwife's instructions. They will probably tell you how to continue and will very likely suggest these two popular recipes which are simple to prepare and medically recommended.

For a baby from Four Days to One Month Old:

Cows' milk (pasteurised)	..	..	5 ozs. (¼ pint)
Boiled water ..	..	..	5 ozs. (¼ pint)
Demerara sugar	..	..	1 tablespoonful

For a baby from One Month old onwards:

Cows' milk (pasteurised)	..	20 ozs. (1 pint)
Boiled water ..	..	10 ozs. (½ pint)
Sugar ..	..	..	3 tablespoonfuls

These amounts make 10 ozs. and 30 ozs. of food respectively, but more or less can be prepared by varying the amounts of the ingredients, but keeping to the same proportions. As baby grows, reduce the sugar gradually and replace the water by milk until, at three months old, undiluted, unsweetened milk is being given.

To Mix the Food.

Bring the milk rapidly to the boil, add the sugar and then the cold boiled water. Well stir with a scalded spoon and pour the mixture into a scalded jug. Cover the jug immediately and cool rapidly. As each feed becomes due pour out the required amount and heat it by standing the bottle in hot water.

The Amount to Give.

The amount of food a baby needs during the twenty-four hours, should be much the same whether he is

completely breast-fed, partly breast- and partly bottle-
fed or bottle-fed entirely, but some babies tend to take
more at one feed than another.   If you are bottle feeding
your baby it is useful to have a guide to which you can
refer and try to keep if baby will do so happily.   Here is
a simple one based on the child's weight rather than his
age, which is usually considered the best way to judge
the amount he needs.

You multiply baby's weight (in pounds) by $2\frac{1}{2}$ and
divide that answer by the number of feeds he has in
twenty-four hours.   The result gives you the amount of
food (in ounces) to offer him at each feed.

For easy reference this is set out in the following table,
and is based on giving five feeds in the day.

Baby's weight	Number of feeds per day	Amount required at each feed	Amount required in 24 hours
6 lbs.	5	3 ozs.	15 ozs.
7 lbs.	5	$3\frac{1}{2}$,,	$17\frac{1}{2}$,,
8 lbs.	5	4 ,,	20 ,,
9 lbs.	5	$4\frac{1}{2}$,,	$22\frac{1}{2}$,,
10 lbs.	5	5 ,,	25 ,,
11 lbs.	5	$5\frac{1}{2}$,,	$27\frac{1}{2}$,,
12 lbs.	5	6 ,,	30 ,,
13 lbs.	5	$6\frac{1}{2}$,,	$32\frac{1}{2}$,,
14 lbs.	5	7 ,,	35 ,,
15 lbs.	5	$7\frac{1}{2}$,,	$37\frac{1}{2}$,,
16 lbs.	5	8 ,,	40 ,,

You will see that each time baby gains a pound he needs
half an ounce more food at every one of his five feeds.

Cod-liver Oil and Fruit Juices

Each day from the age of one month old, baby needs
either fresh or concentrated fruit juice and a little cod- or
halibut-liver oil just as the breast-fed baby does.

Give the cod-liver oil with a teaspoon for two reasons.
The first, because baby will have to take it this way
when he is a little older, and if he is accustomed to it
from infancy it will make it easier for him and for you
later on; the second because oil being lighter than milk,

some of it will get left on the sides of the bottle if you try to mix it in with the food. That will mean baby may go short and the bottle will be more difficult to cleanse.

Feeding Utensils

Be sure to keep all baby's feeding utensils well boiled and scrupulously clean. Immediately after being used rinse the feeding bottle through with cold water. Then wash it in warm soap and water and rinse again. Teats after use should be rubbed inside and out with salt and then well rinsed in cold water, placed on a saucer and covered with a cup.

Baby's bottle should be boiled up once a day. To prevent it from breaking fold it in a cloth, place it in a pan of cold water and bring the water slowly to boiling point. Allow it to boil for five minutes. Then leave it in the water in which it has been boiled until wanted.

Teats may be boiled also. Indeed, it is better that they should be, but since boiling impoverishes rubber, they should only be dropped into the boiling water, boiled for a moment and then placed on a clean dry saucer and covered with their cup.

CHAPTER IX

MIXED FEEDING AND WEANING

MIXED feeding means giving baby some additional food along with his usual breast feed or his usual bottle feed.

It is the first step towards a solid diet. In the early stages, all new foods should be very smooth in texture. If they are lumpy they may make baby heave and turn him against them.

Mixed feeding generally commences two or three months before weaning proper and goes on during it, but where a baby has to be weaned from the breast very early in life, then mixed feeding commences after he has been weaned.

The Age to Start

A normal baby can make a start on mixed feeding when he reaches three or four months old. Until then, no food other than the breast (or bottle), fruit juices and cod-liver oil is needed. After the third or fourth month baby's extras begin to form a very important part of his diet (Fig. 40).

Weaning can, of course, take place at any period of breast-feeding, but the usual age to start substituting artificial feeds for the breast is between six and seven months. Much, though, depends upon the mother and her child. Some babies take to weaning more easily and at a rather earlier age than others; some mothers are obliged to give up breast-feeding sooner than others.

Mixed Feeding

The secret of success lies in introducing the new foods gradually, along with the breast or bottle feeds, and not in place of them. Only the smallest amounts should be

Fig 40

offered at first, and you should give baby plenty of time to get accustomed to one kind of food before going on to another.

You must be prepared, too, to meet with many refusals on his part, and to have to persevere gently until he gets used to the new tastes and the new textures. Some babies are very conservative. They will close their mouths tightly when being offered anything they are not accustomed to, and promptly spit it out if the taste or the texture, or both, is not what they had expected. But, after two or three attempts on subsequent days, they begin to change their minds and are soon eating what is offered with great relish. Never be tempted to use force though. If a new food is refused, never mind, just try again the next day and then the next. It is a good plan to start off while the child is hungry, but be careful to steer clear of upsets and scenes. Those are the last things you want at baby's mealtimes.

How to Begin.

It is best to begin mixed feeding by giving a little baby cereal immediately before the 10 a.m. feed and again before the 6 p.m. feed giving a different cereal in the evening from that given in the morning, and some bone and vegetable broth and vegetable purée before the 2 p.m. feed.

At four to five months old give a taste of egg yolk three times weekly with a buttered rusk at 10 a.m. and baby cereal or strained porridge on the other days. At 2 p.m. increase the broth and give it on alternate days now with a little egg yolk or bone marrow the other days. Each day give some sieved vegetable and as a second course, a little milk pudding, custard or baked or stewed apple pulp and finish with a small breast or bottle feed of about 4 ozs. At 6 p.m. give a finger of brown bread and butter before baby's breast or bottle feed.

FIRST FEEDING CHART

Feeding at 3 to 4 Months Old

6 a.m.	Usual breast- or bottle-feed.
10 a.m.	1 teaspoonful of baby cereal followed by the usual breast- or bottle-feed.
2 p.m.	1 teaspoonful of bone and vegetable broth with 1 teaspoonful of vegetable purée followed by the usual breast- or bottle-feed.
6 p.m.	1 teaspoonful of baby cereal followed by the usual breast- or bottle-feed.
10 p.m.	Usual breast- or bottle-feed. Increase each new food gradually.

Feeding at 4 to 5 Months Old

6 a.m.	Usual breast- or bottle-feed.
10 a.m.	On alternate days give a buttered rusk with 1 teaspoonful of egg yolk, and baby cereal or strained porridge followed by a small breast- or bottle-feed when milk is given with the cereal.
2 p.m.	Half a teacupful of broth three times weekly and some egg yolk or bone marrow four times weekly. 2 dessertspoonfuls of sieved or puréed vegetables. 1 teaspoonful of milk pudding or custard with 1 teaspoonful of stewed or baked apple or prune pulp and followed by a breast- or bottle-feed of about 4 ozs.
6 p.m.	Finger of brown bread and butter spread with the jelly part of jam, or marmalade followed by breast- or bottle-feed.
10 p.m.	Usual breast- or bottle-feed.

Feeding at 5 to 6 Months Old

6 a.m.	Usual breast- or bottle-feed.
10 a.m.	As for 4 to 5 months old, increasing the amounts still further and giving a little stewed fruit now and again.
2 p.m.	As for 4 to 5 months old but start with a buttered rusk and add a little grated cheese to the broth and give 1 teaspoonful scraped, steamed liver or soft herring roes with the vegetables.
6 p.m.	As for 4 to 5 months old but start with a buttered rusk and give a small sponge finger now and again.
10 p.m.	Usual breast- or bottle-feed.

Each Day.—Sips of warm boiled water between feeds from a teaspoon. 1 teaspoonful of cod-liver oil. The strained juice from $\frac{1}{4}$ increasing to $\frac{3}{4}$ of an orange, or concentrated fruit juice according to instructions on the bottle, well diluted with boiled water.

At five to six months old the following additions can be given:— A little stewed apple occasionally at 10 a.m., a little grated cheese on the broth and scraped steamed liver or soft herring roes at 2 p.m. with vegetables.

The other feeds at 6 a.m., 6 p.m. and 10 p.m. are much the same as for from four to five months old.

During the whole of mixed feeding the amounts of each additional food is increased gradually. A buttered rusk can now be given before each of the three main day-time feeds and when baby nears the age of six months old you can consider the question of weaning. Mixed feeding will go on just the same throughout the weaning period, the only difference that still more new foods will be gradually introduced in gradually increasing amounts.

Weaning

Like everything else connected with mothercraft, weaning should be a very gradual process, then neither baby's stomach nor your breasts notice what is happening, and there is no fear of any upset to him, or to you.

You can either start to wean baby at five to six months old and take eight weeks over the process, or you can wait another month and begin when he is six to seven months old. In this case you should take four weeks to wean. In the first case you drop one breast-feed per fortnight; in the second, you drop one breast-feed per week. In place of every breast-feed you drop, you give baby an equivalent amount of artificial food from a bottle, a cup and spoon, or a small cup. The sucking instinct is very strong in babyhood and most babies derive a great deal of comfort and satisfaction from being allowed to take their milk from a bottle especially at bed-time so there is no need to be in a hurry to get baby to drink from a cup.

WEANING IN OUTLINE
1st Period

6 a.m.	Breast-feed.
10 a.m.	Breast-feed.

* 2 p.m.	8 ozs. of artificial food.
6 p.m.	Breast-feed.
10 p.m.	Breast-feed.

2nd Period

6 a.m.	Breast-feed.
*10 a.m.	8 ozs. of artificial food.
2 p.m.	Breast-feed.
* 6 p.m.	8 ozs. of artificial food.
10 p.m.	Breast-feed.

3rd Period

6 a.m.	Breast-feed.
10 a.m.	8 ozs. of artificial food.
2 p.m.	8 ozs. of artificial food.
6 p.m.	8 ozs. of artificial food.
10 p.m.	Breast-feed.

4th Period

6 a.m.	8 ozs. of artificial food.
10 a.m.	8 ozs. of artificial food.
2 p.m.	8 ozs. of artificial food.
6 p.m.	8 ozs. of artificial food.
10 p.m.	Breast-feed.

5th Period

Five artificial feeds of 8 ozs. each.

Any recognised brand of dried milk can be used for the artificial feeds, or if you prefer you can give undiluted cows' milk, provided you are sure of your supply and obtain it from a reliable dairy or farm.

Pasteurised milk (Tuberculin Tested if possible) delivered in bottles should always be used for giving to babies and children, and as double precaution it is wise to bring all their milk rapidly to boiling point, pour it into a scalded jug, cover it immediately and then cool it as quickly as you can.

During the whole of the weaning period, mixed feeding continues and increases are made both in the amount and the variety of foods given.

* If you are going to take eight weeks over weaning baby, and make the change every fortnight instead of every week, give slightly less food at those feeds marked * in the first two periods, unless baby weighs 16 lbs. or over.

Dropping the Feeds.

The first week of weaning (or the first fortnight, according to whether you employ the weekly or the fortnightly method) you give a breast-feed as usual at 6 a.m., 10 a.m., 6 p.m. and 10 p.m.   At 2 p.m. give baby a feed of pasteurised cows' milk or full-cream dried milk.

The second week (or fortnight) you breast-feed him at 6 a.m., 2 p.m. and 10 p.m. and give the new food at both the 10 a.m. and again at the 6 p.m. feed.

By the third week (or fortnight) your breasts should be secreting much less. You now breast-feed baby at 6 a.m. and at 10 p.m. only, giving him milk-feeds at 10 a.m., 2 p.m. and 6 p.m.

The fourth week (or fortnight) you breast-feed once a day only at 10 p.m. and give the milk feeds at 6 a.m., 10 a.m., 2 p.m. and 6 p.m. At the end of this week (or fortnight) no breast-feeds are given; baby is weaned.

By now the amount of milk secreted by the breasts should be almost negligible, and if they are left quietly alone, what is left should dry up without the slightest discomfort. There should be no need to take salts or to bind the breasts, but if there is any uncomfortable feeling of fullness as the weaning period draws to an end, drinking less fluid for a few days should help to get rid of the surplus milk that causes this.

How to Go On

At six to seven months old the egg yolk is increased gradually to four teaspoonfuls, and the cereal and vegetables both increase again. As a change from broth you can give red meat gravy from a roast joint. A little steamed, boned and mashed white fish and finely minced meat can be introduced in small quantities and gradually increased ; also a little mashed, ripe banana. Water to drink can take the place of milk sometimes at 2 p.m.

Although baby may be taking some of his feeds quite nicely from a cup, it is a good plan to still give the last two from either the breast or the bottle because sleeping habits in infancy are closely linked with a child's natural sucking instinct.

At seven to eight months old meal times can change, as you will see from Baby's Third Feeding Chart printed on page 152. On waking, baby has a fruit juice drink.

SECOND FEEDING CHART

Feeding at 6 to 7 Months Old

6 a.m.	Breast- or bottle-feed.
10 a.m.	Rusk and butter and 2-4 teaspoonfuls of egg yolk three times a week. On the other (alternate) days give 2 tablespoonfuls of baby cereal or strained porridge and a little stewed fruit now and again. Follow with breast- or bottle-feed.
2 p.m.	Start with 1 tablespoonful of finely minced meat or liver or steamed and boned fish or broth sprinkled with grated cheese. 2 tablespoonfuls of sieved or mashed vegetables or vegetable purée. Follow with a little milk pudding or custard with baked or stewed apple or prune pulp. Now and again give some mashed ripe banana. A small milk feed or some water to drink.
6 p.m.	Buttered rusk spread with honey or the jelly part of jam or a yeast extract. Or a thin brown bread sandwich. A sponge finger now and again or a biscuit. Breast- or bottle-feed to follow.
10 p.m.	Breast- or bottle-feed.

Each Day.—1 teaspoonful of cod-liver oil. The strained juice of the whole of a medium-sized orange, or concentrated fruit juice according to directions on the bottle, well diluted with boiled water.

You can either give the strained juice of a whole orange, or some concentrated orange juice, rose hip syrup or blackcurrant juice well diluted with water.

In some homes, baby has breakfast with the family, in others he has breakfast on his own either before or after everyone else has finished. The best plan is to let him take his place, first on mother's knee and later in his high chair at the table now so that good table manners are learned gradually by observation and example.

Breakfast starts with a rusk or crust of brown bread spread with butter. Follow this three times a week by half, increasing gradually to the whole of a coddled,

Dinner at eight months old.

poached or scrambled egg or a little crisply fried bacon
that has been crumbled or finely cut up before serving.
Some children prefer the yolk of a hard boiled egg to a
softly boiled one, and this may always be given when that
is so.   On the other days of the week give a baby cereal
or some thin strained porridge with added milk and a
little brown sugar.   Vary the cereal giving those made
from barley, oats and wheat in rotation and increasing
the amounts as baby grows, but remember that only small
helpings are needed for quite a time and that the child's
appetite should never be satisfied with the first course.
Now and again give a little stewed fruit or some mashed
really ripe banana and about 8 ozs. of milk to drink.

For baby's dinner, give small amounts of finely minced
or very well cut up beef, lamb, liver, chicken, rabbit, well
cooked tripe, or a little steamed and boned white fish, or
soft fish roes, or some broth sprinkled with grated cheese
each day.   A little mashed potato with some other root
or green cooked vegetable is served with this course.
The vegetable should be sieved, strained or puréed.
Follow with some milk pudding or custard with fruit such
as pulped prunes or stewed or baked apple, or a tiny
helping of steamed (but not boiled) pudding like lemon
sponge, or castle pudding.   Baby can have water or fruit
juice drink with this meal.

Tea-supper consists of a hard crust of brown bread with
butter and honey or the jelly part of marmalade or jam
or some thin brown bread sandwiches of the same with a
finger of cake or shortbread to follow and about 8 ozs. of
milk.

Most babies give up the 10 p.m. bottle feed between
nine and twelve months old, either by sleeping through
or having the amount reduced gradually.   Much depends
on your baby's own inclination here coupled with his
weight and general well being.   Some seem to need the
comfort of this last feed more than others. Indeed, some
mothers continue to give a breast feed then for a time

THIRD FEEDING CHART

Feeding at 7 to 12 Months Old

On Waking: Juice of a whole orange or concentrated fruit juice according to the amounts printed on the bottle, well diluted with water.

Breakfast: Rusk or crust of brown bread spread with butter. Half, increasing to a whole coddled, poached or scrambled egg or a little crisply fried and chopped up bacon three times a week. Baby cereal or thin strained porridge four times a week. Now and again a little stewed fruit or mashed, ripe banana. 8 ozs. of milk to drink.

Dinner: Small amounts of finely minced or well cut up beef, lamb, liver, chicken or rabbit, or well cooked tripe, or boned white fish or broth sprinkled with grated cheese served with some vegetable purée or sieved vegetables and a little mashed potato. A little milk pudding or custard with sieved prunes or baked or stewed apple, or other stewed fruit without pips or seeds, or a tiny helping of castle or a lightly steamed (not boiled) pudding now and again. Water to drink.

Tea-Supper: Rusks or a hard crust of brown bread with butter and honey or the jelly part of marmalade or jam, or thin sandwiches made from brown bread. Plain madeira cake, or a sponge finger or piece of shortbread. 8 ozs. of milk to drink.

10 p.m. Bottle-feed of about 8 ozs.

Each Day Cod-liver oil.

The 10 p.m. feed is usually given up between nine and twelve months old by gradually giving less and less milk then. When this feed is reduced or discontinued, give a little more milk during the day to make up.

because they find it helps their baby to settle peacefully for the rest of the night.   There is no harm at all in this if it suits both mother and child.

Other babies, on the other hand, will have weaned themselves from the 10 p.m. feed before they reach the age of nine months old.

Baby's Milk

If you give liquid cows' milk to your baby it should be obtained from a reliable dairy and every effort made to obtain pasteurised milk (Tuberculin Tested if possible). Have it delivered in sealed bottles to your door if you can, and as a double precaution bring it rapidly to boiling point, pour it into a scalded jug, cover it immediately and then cool it quickly.   The quick cooling is of great importance.   Treated this way, the vitamin content is interfered with as little as possible.

CHAPTER X

FEEDING DIFFICULTIES

WHILE the majority of mothers and babies get on very well indeed with few, if any, real feeding difficulties, there are others who are not so fortunate. As a rule, it is only a small matter to put things right, but it can be very worrying if baby does not take well, and you are not sure why, for one thing, or how to remedy it for another.

Baby's Early Troubles

Baby's early feeding troubles divide themselves into two headings. Let us see what they each are.

1. The child is either disinclined to suck, or else he is too sleepy to take his food well.
2. He shows every inclination to feed well, but he experiences difficulty in getting the food.

Won't Suck Well.

If you think baby's case comes under the first category then before you do anything else you should assure yourself that he is perfectly well in himself. If he is not, he is certain to be off his food. Ask yourself : Does he seem seedy, hot or feverish ? Is he suffering from diarrhoea or sickness ? Is he very flushed or unduly pale ? Has he noisy breathing or is he breathing very fast ? If the answer is " yes " to any of these things you should call your doctor in.

But if, as is most probably the case, there is nothing wrong with your baby's health, then before he even begins to feed, you must see that he is properly awake. No baby can take well if he is half asleep, and a lot of the feeding difficulties of the early weeks are due to this.

Let baby lie and kick away on your knee or else in his cot or pram for five or six minutes before you attempt to feed him, undressing him (either partly or wholly) if necessary and if it is a warm day so that the air will act as a stimulus to his system and rouse him thoroughly.

Having started baby off well, you must guard against his falling soundly asleep before he has taken enough. There are two causes for a baby dropping into a sound

Make sure that baby is really awake before he is fed.

sleep during a feed like this. The first is that he may be too warm and too comfortable in his mother's arms, and the second that he may have had a long stretch of crying before the feed. This would have made him so tired that he finds it impossible to stay awake once the first pangs of hunger have been satisfied.

While it is right that baby should feel secure and comfortable in your arms when he feeds, you must try and keep him sufficiently awake to take consistently. Where his trouble is persistent crying before a feed the remedy is to reduce the intervals between each feed changing from four-hourly to three-hourly feeding or even better, feed him when he wakes and cries for it until he is happier and better satisfied. Demand-feeding, as we call this, is described on page 126.

Can't Suck Well.

Maybe, though, your baby is willing enough to suck but has difficulty in doing so with ease.

There are several reasons for this state of affairs and any one or a combination of two or more may be responsible, so we will consider them in order.

(a) Baby may have difficulty in grasping the nipple. This may be due to the breasts being engorged (or too full of milk), or to the nipple being a poor shape.

If the breasts are too full it is quite impossible for a baby to get the nipple far enough back into his mouth to enable his jaws to munch up and down on the dark skin surrounding its base. Unless he can do this, he cannot draw the milk properly. Fortunately, it is easy to empty the breasts a little by drawing off some of the milk. The method is explained on page 129.

The nipple must reach nearly to the back of his throat. If it is not a good shape then in the very simple words of one mother you must " let the baby take an extra good mouthful of breast." He will want to get a piece roughly the size of a penny into his mouth. Then he will be able to suck easily. Where the nipples are inverted it may be necessary to feed through a nipple shield, but this should only be used as a last resort.

(b) Baby may bury his nose in the breast. This interferes with his breathing and will always make him restless. Hold the flesh away from his nose to give him plenty of breathing space.

(c) Baby may be suffering from snuffles. If he is the best thing is to ask your doctor for some simple remedy to dry up the secretion. Nasal drops are often ordered for this in these days.

(d) Baby may be taking too fast or gulping down air along with his feed and this will give him wind. Use the method of controlling the milk described on page 127 or give baby a little warm boiled water just before his feeds, make sure he is not ravenously hungry when put to the breast, and see that he brings up his wind during and after each feed.

(*e*) He may be suffering from a sore mouth. Usually soreness of the mouth is due to thrush. That is fully dealt with in Chapter XIII.

(*f*) His attention may be distracted by others in the room.

(*g*) The milk may not flow easily owing to the breast being empty or to the milk ducts being blocked, or to the mother withholding the milk unconsciously due to nervousness, anxiety, worry or fear.

The Mother's Troubles

Broadly speaking these come under two headings also.
1. Not enough milk for baby's needs.
2. Pain due to a sore or a cracked nipple.

Short of Milk.

Some mothers make milk more freely and more easily than others. When the supply is low, or where for some reason it fails altogether, it is nearly always possible to increase the amount.

The first thing to do is to drink more fluid and take a richer diet. Drink as much raw milk as you can each day and make into milk puddings and milk soups any that is over.

Have a cup of gruel during the morning and another last thing at night. Take cocoa in place of tea and coffee, and sip a glass of water, barley water, lemonade or fruit juice and water each time you feed baby.

Eat more cheese, more meat, more foods or preparations containing vitamin B, more fat and more sugar for a short time.

Make certain that each breast is completely emptied at every feed, and gently massage away any milk that may remain after baby has finished.

In bad cases it may be necessary to change from

four-hourly to three-hourly feeds for a few days until conditions begin to improve, and twice a day, one hour before a feed is due, stimulate the breasts by bathing them alternately in very hot and very cold water.

Until the milk increases in quantity naturally, small complementary feeds of some artificial food should be given to make up, but before you know how much artificial food to give your baby, you must find out by test-weighing, how much breast milk he has already taken. This is quite simple.

To Test-weigh.

You will need a pair of baby scales, a pencil and some paper.

1. Change baby's napkin, weigh him and write down the weight carefully.
2. Give the feed in the usual way.
3. Without changing the napkin (even if it is soiled) weigh baby again.
4. Subtract the first weight from this second one. The answer will be in ounces and this represents the amount of food (in ounces) that baby has had.

Since most babies take more at one feed than at another, it is best to test-weigh at each feed for one whole day, and then add up the amounts. The result of that will give you the full total taken in any one day, e.g.

6 a.m. baby took	5	ozs.
10 a.m.	,,	$4\frac{1}{2}$	,,
2 p.m.	,,	4	,,
6 p.m.	,,	3	,,
10 p.m.	,,	$3\frac{1}{2}$	,,

At all feeds   20 ozs.
$$20 \div 5 = 4$$

If his present weight is 12 lbs. he needs 6 ozs. at each feed or 30 ozs. in a day. Therefore he is going short of 10 ozs. during the day, or an average of 2 ozs. at each feed.

Amount of Food.

The amount of food a baby needs varies according to his weight and not according to his age. It is set out in detail on page 140.

Complementary Feeding.

Where you have to give a complementary feed you can use National Dried Milk, unsweetened evaporated milk or one of the dried baby milks on the market, made up according to instructions on the tin or packet.

Or, alternatively, pasteurised, Tuberculin Tested cows' milk may be used after it has been diluted with water and some sugar added:

Cows' milk* (pasteurised)	..	..	2 ozs.
Boiled water ..	..	..	1 oz.
Brown sugar ..	..	..	1 level teaspoonful

* All liquid cows' milk should as a double precaution be scalded at home by bringing it rapidly to boiling point, pouring it into a scalded jug, securely covering it and then cooling it as quickly as possible.

This amount makes 3 ozs. of milk mixture. You can make up more or less by increasing or decreasing the ingredients in the same proportions. To put it another way: Use half as much water as milk, and as many level teaspoonfuls of sugar as you add ounces of water.

If you have no scales and are unable to test-weigh baby, then give two or three ounces of artificial food after each breast feed, varying the amount (slightly more or slightly less) until baby is happy and thriving.

Cracked and Sore Nipples.

Not only is a sore nipple exceedingly painful to a mother while her baby is at her breast, but it can be a potential source of danger; germs can gain entrance to the breast through the injury (tiny though it may be), and set up inflammation in the breast tissue which, if neglected, may turn to an abscess.

At the very first sign of any soreness, buy yourself a nursing nipple shield from your chemist and use this over the nipple when feeding baby for the time being. This will protect the skin from the friction of his sucking. After each feed carefully wash and dry both nipples and paint the affected one with a little one-per-cent aluminium acetate. Then cover it with a pad of sterile gauze of several thicknesses, or a square of clean stout linen which you have made germ-free by scorching it before the fire immediately before using. Aluminium acetate stings when applied, but as stated elsewhere it is so good that it is well worth the temporary discomfort.

Another preparation you can use in the same way is Friar's Balsam, but it is sticky, and less rapid in action. Both are quite harmless to the baby, but the nipples should be carefully washed before he feeds.

Anything more than a very slight crack or sore should receive a doctor's attention. You should also see your doctor if the part is not practically healed within about twenty-four hours, and always right away, if there are any signs of soreness, pain, heat, throbbing or redness of the breast itself, since these are the warning signs that an abscess is threatening or perhaps even beginning. If medical treatment is received early enough in breast trouble of this kind, a quick cure nearly always results in these days, and it may not be necessary even temporarily to keep the baby from feeding at that breast.

Later Difficulties

Once you have dispelled the early feeding difficulties, if there have been any, everything goes along smoothly as a rule until baby reaches the mixed feeding stage and various additions begin to make their appearance in his diet. Some babies take to mixed feeding without any trouble at all ; others dislike new foods at first.

More often than not, it is the different textures of the food rather than the strange tastes that they take exception to, but they soon get over their dislikes, especially if their mothers do not show concern, but treat the

A child will sometimes take a dislike to food he once enjoyed.

whole matter in a happy, understanding and quite unemotional way. This does not mean that a little gentle perseverance is not necessary. It is, very often, but if after trying the particular food in question on three or four days in succession the baby does not begin to get used to it and it cannot be offered in any other form, then the best thing to do is to omit it for a day or two. It will probably be eaten with relish next time.

At a rather later stage still, it is very common for a

F

child to take a sudden and often quite an unaccountable dislike to food that he previously enjoyed. Carrots or cabbage or one of the other vegetables are very frequently the things that are refused, though sometimes it is egg or egg custard. Not infrequently, milk gets left.

It is better not to be too strict about this, otherwise it merely results in the mother either coaxing or insisting, and the child refusing. That is upsetting to both.

The wisest course is to alter the menus a little. Milk should never be forced. Where it is not drunk, often a child will take some of it in the form of milk soup or made into jellies or as pudding. When this is done it is important to give water to drink in its place. When food is left on plates the wisest course is to offer rather less at meal times.

Remember that a hungry child will always eat, but remember, too, that food should be nicely cooked and attractively served. Never make the mistake of mashing up the various items together on one plate and covering all with gravy or milk. Instead, put small helpings of the different foods in separate little piles, and if one of the piles is left, never mind. A little food that is enjoyed is far better than a lot that is hated. Emotional upsets are things to steer very clear of at mealtimes where little children are concerned.

CHAPTER XI

MOTHERING AND TRAINING

LIKE all babies, yours is going to need a great deal of love. Without maternal love of the right kind your baby cannot possibly be as happy and as bonny as he should be. No child can. Mothering therefore is going to play a very big role in his early life.

But you must be careful not to confuse mothering and mother love with spoiling. They are two totally different things. When you mother baby, you help him. You instil him with comfort, with a sense of security and with the knowledge that he is both loved and wanted and is, indeed, a very dear member of your home and your home circle. Mothering develops character. It makes for happiness and harmony between parent and child, and between that child and the world. Spoiling does exactly the opposite. It breeds discontent and unhappiness and makes life very much harder and much more complicated.

Before Birth

During the nine prenatal months while baby was in the womb, you were mothering him every moment of the day and night in a very special and intimate way. You nourished him with food, you provided him with warmth and quite unconsciously you rocked him to and fro as you moved and walked about.

After Birth

After his birth there is, for every baby, a partial continuance of the prenatal state. This is shown very clearly in the way a new born child sleeps away most of his time and only really rouses himself to be bathed and fed, or when he feels cold, or hungry.

During your little one's early days in the world, therefore, try and make your mothering match the kind he enjoyed before he was born. This you will be able to do if you remember that baby's three first needs where mothering is concerned are:

1. To be able to feel the warmth from your own body.
2. To be able to get his food without trouble or annoyance.
3. To experience some kind of rocking movement.

At Feeding Time

When you are feeding him, see that he lies comfortably in your arms and hold him quite closely to you so that he may sense the comforting warmth from your own body. But do not make him so comfortable that instead of sucking he falls off into a deep sleep.

Next, make certain that you hold the feeding breast so that he can get the milk without any annoyance or vexation on his part. Keep the flesh well away from his nose. Give him plenty of room to breathe. Make sure that you get the nipple right far back into his mouth. A young baby does not suck as we understand sucking. If you watch yours critically you will see that he munches at the breast, working his jaws up and down on that ring of dark flesh which surrounds each nipple base. Every time his jaws close on this they send a jet of milk forward into the nipple and, of course, out into baby's mouth.

This is one reason why as we have seen in an earlier chapter, you should not attempt to feed your baby while your breasts are very full of milk, but to draw some of it off first. They must be soft enough to allow this dark flesh to be drawn right inside his mouth between his upper and his lower jaws (Fig. 36). Few mothers realise this at first.   Once they do, they seldom have difficulty in getting their babies to take well.

See, always, that baby's hands are quite free to caress the breasts when he wishes to or to fondle at the bottle. The act of feeding should provide a baby with emotional

Don't be afraid to rock baby sometimes.

as well as physical satisfaction, and this very tender gesture on his part is a charming and natural instinct. It is one that should be encouraged rather than thwarted or hindered in any way.

Rocking Baby

There is a lot to be said for the old rocking chair.

Children love being rocked ; and to sit and rock your baby in your arms and provide him with some of that movement to which he became so accustomed before birth is just another way of demonstrating your mother-love.   It is a very good way, too, and it is one that your child can appreciate, and one that he will enjoy.

The same applies to rocking him to sleep when he is sad.   Children find it very comforting and very soothing to be rocked, and while we agree it is a mistake to get a baby into the way of expecting to be rocked off to sleep every time and as a habitual thing, it is equally certain that no rocking at all is just as bad.   The best plan is to let yours settle off to sleep by himself when he will, and reserve the rocking for those times when he is fretful and sad.   You will find that his demands here are very reasonable.   And this will be because you are encouraging a calm, placid state of mind in your baby as opposed to a worried and a frustrated one.

In very much the same way you need not be afraid of picking him up now and again and carrying him round with you.   It is a great mistake for a mother to imagine that a young baby should spend all his time on his own in his cot or his pram.

Mothering Hour

However busy you are, try to set aside some time, at least, each day, for sole devotion to your little one. Many mothers make this time the hour after tea, when the bulk of the day's work is done and the warmth of a winter fire, or the cool calm of a summer evening are so inviting.

Sometimes, at first, you can let baby lie on your knee. hampered by as little clothing as the season will permit so that he can kick and exercise to his heart's content. Sometimes you can sing to him in low soft tones.   Later on you can add words to your songs ; or count " this little pig " on his toes ; or allow him to spring up and

Mothering Hour.

down on your knee. Later still you can introduce the first nursery rhymes as he sits on your lap and learns in his own time and at his own pace, to listen and later to repeat.

Sowing Good Habits

The acquisition of good habits is a thing you cannot rush. It should be very gradual and, moreover, it should be accomplished without any undue emotion so that customs, as time goes on, become accepted as a matter of course.

Few children are dry by day before the age of a year at the very earliest. At night it is often two years and sometimes three, before napkins can be dispensed with for good. Not so many years ago it was the custom to commence training a baby to use his chamber when he was only a few days old, but we now know that this is not a good plan. Serious attempts at habit training should not begin until a child is well able to sit up on his own and is so skilled in balancing that he can perhaps even stand.

Do not, then commence to train baby too earnestly too soon. The nervous mechanism which controls the bowel and bladder is not fully complete until a child is round about two years old, so up till then at least, accidents and mistakes are bound to occur. There may be phases, too, of refusing to sit out, of getting up and toddling away, wanting to play with the receptacle instead of use it, or of doing nothing while on it but almost immediately afterwards, soiling or wetting the clean napkin you have just put on. Another phase through which some children pass is that of having a bowel or bladder action first and asking for the pot a moment or two afterwards instead of the other way about.

The proper way to hold baby out when he is young is described on page 96 and illustrated on the page following. Some mothers have their own way of indicating to baby what is happening by making soft grunting noises when he passes a motion and whispering " wee " as he makes water. The holding out should never be prolonged. If baby does not oblige within two minutes at most, he should be taken off and no remarks passed one way or another. When he is old enough to sit out on his own, place him on his chamber at such times as you think he needs to go, give him a toy to play with, and then leave him alone (but not out of your sight) for most children dislike being looked at while they are having a bowel action.

Early Responsibilities

As your little one grows, so of course mothering must vary. Instead of his depending entirely upon you, you must help him to learn more and more to depend upon himself, by encouraging him in his own efforts, and providing him with opportunities for shouldering a little responsibility.

Roughly, the time to begin is when baby shows an inclination to attempt things on his own. You will notice how independent he wants to become. So far as you can, only help him when it is necessary, or where his self-appointed task is really more than he can manage. Never mind his mistakes. Children learn much from experience, and they enjoy and profit by adventure.

Nearly a Toddler

By the time your baby reaches a year old he should have gained about fourteen pounds over and above his birth weight. He will probably possess six to eight teeth—possibly more, though he could possess less. He should be able to sit alone and it is likely that he will not only be crawling well, but also standing well.

He will be saying Dad-Dad quite clearly and maybe if he is very forward a few simple English words in

F*

addition. He will certainly make many baby sounds and understand a great many things that you say to him. In fact, he will understand much more that you may credit him with, for at this age a baby's brain is very much on the alert. He will appreciate a tin tray

Baby at one year old.

to bang on and he will enjoy bricks to try and build. He may be a trifle shy when it comes to going to strangers, but this need not worry you. It is very natural. He will need sixteen hours sleep now out of the twenty-four. His skin should be firm and tanned ; the soft spot in his skull getting very small. His chest should be developing well and his arms and legs beginning to lose their baby curves.

His meals become more varied, and from his first birthday he can learn to hold his own mug. Soon after this he will be wielding his own pusher and spoon. Baby is, in fact, growing up, and growing fast.

CHAPTER XII

GROWING UP

MOST babies begin to crawl before they begin to walk but here and there a child will walk first and take to crawling later. It makes no difference really and if yours wants to try his feet before going down on all fours you can let him.

Learning to Walk

If baby has been correctly fed, is healthy and strong and not too fat, it is best to leave him to his own inclinations where walking is concerned and allow him to toddle round holding on to chairs or anything else that is handy. The exercise will be good for him. You can help him too by taking his hand when he wants you to, but it is as much a mistake to try and force him on to his legs as it is to keep him off them altogether.

You must not get worried if baby starts to clamber and climb. Give him a little stool or a big cardboard box and then he will not want to get up on to the chairs where he might fall off and hurt himself. All the same, be prepared for a few bumps and tumbles. They are common at toddling age when a child is learning to keep his balance and not finding it very easy to do so.

Danger

You will have to watch baby carefully now for he will be round the corner and out of your sight in a moment. But it is no good trying to keep him in his play pen for all his waking hours. He will only grizzle and cry if you do so. He wants and he needs to be out and exploring, and because of this, it is very necessary to see that he cannot come to harm.

Fires and fireplaces must have very strong guards, too firm for him to move.   Electric light switches and cables should be out of his reach.   Knives and scissors, needles and pins, and anything else that is sharp must be right

He will want to climb.

out of his sight and kept out of his way.   Windows need bars, gates a safety catch, and the top of the stairs some gate or device to stop him from falling downstairs.   Gas taps should be adjusted so that they are too stiff for him to turn on, and matches must never be left lying about.

Remember that saucepan handles and the kettle spout

Keep saucepan handles towards the wall.

can be a danger if they jut out over the stove. Turn them inwards to the wall and keep them on the back of the cooking stove where baby will not grab at them and tip their contents all over himself. If he does he may get scalded, perhaps beyond recovery. See that the teapot is in a safe place, and never forget that if a child tugs at the tablecloth he may easily pull cups of boiling hot tea on to the floor—perhaps on to himself.

Speech

Babies vary so much in learning to talk that it is impossible to lay down any hard and fast rules. First children are slower, as a rule, than those where there are others already in the home. The second baby, therefore, is generally talking well at a younger age than the first.

Never use " baby language " when speaking to your child. He will learn to talk quicker if you speak to him well and use sentences of few words. " Get up ? " is better than " It is time to get up and dress now." And " Out with Mummy ? " or even just " Out ? " instead of " Would you like to come for a walk with me ? "

Where talking is delayed beyond the age of three years, a doctor should be consulted, to make sure that baby's hearing is all right. Probably there is nothing to worry about, but now and again there is, so if you think your baby is backwards in starting to talk take particular notice of how he responds when you speak to him. If he appears to take no notice or does not do as you say as a general thing, you should get a medical opinion without delay, to make sure he is not deaf.

Stuttering

It is by no means uncommon for a child to start to stutter when he gets to about three years old and it is hardly ever serious at this age when he does. It is generally due to ideas coming into his mind faster than he can formulate words to express them. After a while

the trouble passes and should not return, but no attention
should be paid to the stuttering while it lasts.   Instead,
listen quietly to what he has to say, talk to him rather
more slowly than usual and pronounce your own words
extra clearly.

Good impressions have lasting results.

Playthings

It is surprising what simple playthings will amuse a
toddler of a year or eighteen months old.   A tin mug
with a spoon keeps him occupied for a long time.   Small
boxes, clothes pegs, brightly coloured bricks become just
as firm favourites as soft cuddly toys.   There is no need

to get anything expensive. It is bright colours and playthings that will make a noise that baby will love.

Everything he has, though, will go to his mouth, so see that what you do give him will not be harmful when he sucks it.   Avoid very small toys that could get wedged in this throat, and all those with sharp edges or paint that will chip or peel off.

A little later on your child will begin to enjoy playing with some water, pouring it from cup to cup.   Water play is very good for children, particularly those with any kind of emotional upset.   It will keep them happy for hours.

Meal-times

From quite a young age a little child begins to receive impressions connected with meal-times, and these can have very lasting results.   The way in which the table is set, therefore, becomes just as important as table manners themselves.   So always remember to take great care to see that the cloth—where one is used—is as spotless as possible, that table mats are neatly arranged, that bibs are clean, that the butter-dish is complete with its own butter-knife, and that the jam pot or jar (where jam is not put out into dishes) is placed on a saucer with a spoon to itself.   And from the time baby begins to sit up to the table in his high chair, his hands and face should always be washed and the hair tidied.

Until he has learned to wield his spoon and pusher, meal-times are bound to be rather messy from an adult point of view, you will find.   But that is only to be expected, so make suitable provision for this in the form of something to cover the floor just under baby's chair.

As a child grows older, he should be encouraged to assist in handing dishes to others as well as helping himself.   In this, as well as in everything else, remember that his greatest teacher will be the good examples that you yourself set him.

FOURTH FEEDING CHART

Feeding at 1 to 2 Years Old

On Waking   Orange juice well diluted with water.

Breakfast   Cereal or thin porridge with milk. (In summer give a little stewed fruit with crisp toast instead.) 1 small rasher of crisply fried or grilled bacon, or a few breadcrumbs fried in bacon fat or a coddled egg, or a little lightly-scrambled egg, or a little lightly-cooked pounded up liver. Toast or brown bread with butter and honey, or syrup, or the jelly part of marmalade or jam. 8 ozs. of milk to drink, including that used for the cereal or porridge.

Dinner   A little pounded and boned fish, or soft roes, or chicken, or rabbit, or scraped beef or lamb or mutton, or brains, or Irish stew, or fresh mince, or sweetbreads, or lightly-cooked liver, or well-cooked tripe. Small helping of mashed potato, or mealy jacket potato, and a similar amount of mashed vegetables, or greens. Now and again, grate a little cheese over the vegetables. Milk pudding, or custard and stewed fruit, or a little baked apple, or junket or lightly-steamed pudding, or Castle pudding. Water to drink. 1 teaspoonful of cod-liver oil to follow this meal.

Tea-Supper   Thin brown bread and butter with honey, or the jelly part of jam or marmalade, or fruit jelly, and now and again a taste of grated cheese. A small slice of plain cake, or sponge cake. Milk to drink.

A slice of raw apple or a portion of orange or other similar fruit should be given after meals from the age of eighteen months to act as a tooth-cleansing agent.

Water may be given to drink whenever a child asks for it, and some chocolate and plain boiled sugar sweets in small quantities may be given after dinner.

Under the age of three years all drinking water should be boiled. Until at least five years old, milk should be brought rapidly to boiling point as soon as delivered and then quickly cooled and kept covered in scalded vessels. Pasteurised milk (Tuberculin Tested if possible) is the safest milk for children. It should be obtained from a reliable farm or dairy.

FIFTH FEEDING CHART

Feeding at 2 to 5 Years Old

On Waking   Orange juice or rose hip syrup well diluted with water.

Breakfast   Porridge or breakfast cereal. Scrambled, poached or boiled egg or omelette, or a rasher of crisply fried bacon, or steamed (boned) fish or fish cake, or fish roes, or some liver. Toast or brown bread and butter with honey, marmalade, syrup, jam or vitamin B preparation. Milk to drink. Three or four times a week give a little fresh fruit.

Dinner   Steamed (boned) fish or fish roes; or liver, or rabbit or mutton or beef or chicken (minced or cut up), or cottage pie or Irish stew, or Lancashire hot-pot, or broth with grated cheese. Mashed, baked, steamed or roast potatoes with green or root vegetables. Fresh, stewed or baked fruit with milk pudding or custard or blancmange or junket ; or lightly-steamed pudding, or Castle pudding. Water to drink.

Tea-Supper   Rusks, or toast, or brown bread and butter with honey, jam, marmalade, dripping, cream cheese or vitamin B preparation, or lettuce, cress, egg and cress, or tomato sandwiches. Madeira cake or shortbread or ginger snaps or sponge fingers or jam sponge roll. Milk to drink.

Each Day   1 teaspoonful of cod-liver oil.

These foods are good and may be given in addition :—

Scotch broth, lentil, pea, onion, artichoke, potato, celery and tomato soups, mutton broth. Fish pie and fish and tomatoes. Cold meat (ham, tongue, beef, lamb, liver), haricot mutton, boiled beef with carrots and dumplings, apple pudding, apple snow, batter pudding, chocolate shape.

These foods are bad for children under five :—

Eels, mackerel and all shell fish, pork, veal, goose, duck and game, stringy vegetables such as old runner beans, over-ripe fruit and un-ripe fruit, figs and nuts, tea, coffee, pickles, sauces, vinegar, new bread, muffins, crumpets and rich fruit cake.

A slice of raw apple or a portion of orange or other similar fruit should be given after meals to act as a tooth-cleansing agent.

Give water to drink whenever a child asks for it, and some chocolate and plain boiled sugar sweets in small quantities after dinner.

Sleep

Far too many children between the age of one and five years stay up too late at night. Children need plenty of sleep, and below is a table giving the total number of hours most require at different ages.

Age	Hours sleep needed at night	Hours sleep needed during the day	Total
1–2 years	12–13	3	15–16
2–3 ,,	12–13	2	14–15
3–4 ,,	12–13	1	13–14
4–5 ,,	11–12	Possibly 1	12–13

Until he reaches the age of four or five years old part of baby's sleep will be taken in the daytime.

There is no need to continue to put baby to bed at 6 p.m. now that he is growing older if it will suit your household better to retard his bedtime hour. Sometimes when a child of two or three years goes to bed at six every evening he will wake at six next morning or even before. It may be much more convenient to you if he does not wake up till seven or even seven-thirty, and if you adjust his bedtime hour, making it 7 p.m. instead of 6 p.m., you will probably find he stays asleep later in the morning to balance it up.

It is important to make quite sure that your child does not go to bed in a highly excitable state. Rough and tumble games, pillow fights and exciting stories should be reserved for the earlier parts of the day. Over-excitement just before bedtime and stories which are frightening or over-stimulating are one cause—and a very real cause—of restless nights, fitful slumber and nightmares. Others, are heavy suppers, unhealthy tonsils, adenoid trouble and intestinal worms.

Here is yet another reason which far too often gets overlooked. It concerns children who, perhaps owing to housing conditions, are forced to sleep in their parents' bedrooms when, ideally, they would occupy a room of their own. Children are not always asleep when their elders think they are. Sometimes they partly see or over-hear things that are puzzling and though they may not tell you anything about it, the incident leaves a disturbing impression on their minds.

So, if your child has to sleep in your bedroom, make quite sure that he is soundly asleep when you go to bed.

Dreams

It is difficult to say how old a child is when he first begins to dream, but some undoubtedly dream more than others. The early dreams should be happy, simple little affairs, but round about three and a half years and again a year later, a child often goes through phases when his dreams are far from simple.

He may even get an occasional nightmare, and this despite the fact that he spent the hour before bed time quietly, that you only read to him happy stories of birds and rabbits, that he had no heavy supper and has no adenoid trouble or worms.

Should you hear your little one in a nightmare go in to him and, if he is still asleep, waken him gently, comfort him and let him know that everything is all right because you are there, very near at hand.

Don't ask him what is the matter. There is no point in recalling to his conscious mind what was disagreeable. Let all that fade into the background, and when it has, tuck him up with a toy or a teddy to finish the night in peace.

Remember, though, that children who have been made emotionally tense through upsets, fusses and scenes over habit training, meals and so on, are much more liable to suffer from nightmare than those whose mothers have been, and still are, easy going and placid.

Bedtime Problems

Bedtime problems are common round about two to three years old. Calling out or crying for mother after she has tucked her child up for the night is very common. So, too, is the request for little drinks of water to be brought up to him, or the sudden desire to pass urine soon after he has gone to bed.

It is a mistake to leave your child to cry it out alone.

These and the similar episodes that occur in so many homes where there are children are all signs of some kind of uneasiness in the particular child's mind. The best thing to do when you meet them is to call up to your child now and again from downstairs, so that he realises he is far from alone, and couple this with a gentle but firm command to go to sleep at once. If that is not enough, try spending a few moments in tidying up his room, or sitting down beside him for a minute or two, and then explain that you must go down again now to prepare his breakfast otherwise it may not be ready. Before you go assure him that you are very near to him really, and that he will be able to hear you moving about below.

It is a mistake to be too strict or to leave your child to cry it out alone at such times. That only increases his anxiety, and while it is true that he may drop off to sleep when he is too tired to remain awake, it will not be the calm untroubled slumber that he should enjoy, and that ought to put a happy finish to a happy day.

You want pleasant reflections in your child's mind as sleep approaches, not conflicts and worries. To this end it will help a lot if you always make a practice of warning him as bedtime draws near. Tell him that in a few moments he will have to start putting his toys away and get ready to have his bath. And then, after he is in bed, leave his door open so that he can hear you tidying up. If the evening is dark and he wants a light let him have one.

It is better not to demand or expect absolute silence. It is not natural. In fact, quite a number of children hold a short conversation with themselves, or sing to themselves after they are in bed and when they do it should never be checked, though there is no harm in insisting that this must be done quite softly.

Fear of the Dark

One of the commonest fears of childhood is fear of the dark. Sometimes it comes on as the result of a nightmare or a bad dream ; sometimes it is due to some shadow cast on the wall by the flickering firelight. Or, the wind may be to blame, or a thunderstorm. Sometimes a child is frightened because his mother is afraid, which shows you how very careful you must be never to show fear yourself. Frightening bedtime stories are at the root of many childish fears and so are bits of adult conversation which may have been overheard and wrongly interpreted.

Whatever the cause, the fear can be very real and it

can be very terrifying to a three- or four-year old. Here there is a lot an understanding mother can do to reassure her child and explain away or calm his terror. Besides showing him that it is quite all right and there is nothing to be afraid of, it is a help to leave a light in his room.   If you use a nightlight make certain that it is in a safe place where there is no fear of his touching it.

Provide materials for making things that can be destroyed.

Lies

Most children are highly imaginative.   They fancy all kinds of things.   So it is quite likely that when your baby is three to four years old he will make up strange stories, too, and repeat them to you without having any intention whatever of telling an untruth.

It is much better at these times not to scold or rebuke, but to just let the child see that you realise it is make-believe on his part.

Telling lies in order to get out of trouble is a very different thing.   In this case a child tells a lie because he is afraid to own up to the truth.   Scolding him is not the way to deal with it. That will only teach him to tell a bigger and a better lie next time. All the same, you must teach him not to say what is not true.

Truthfulness and honesty are essential sides to a good character and they are very important traits to develop in your baby. When he tells you a lie, and he knows it to be a lie, the best thing to do is to say quite quietly, " Oh, think again, dear, and this time tell Mummy what really did happen." Then assure him that " That's better," and correct him then and there, quite firmly if needs be, but never harshly and never punish him after he has owned up.

Destructiveness

How often, when he gets to between two and three years old, a baby becomes very destructive ! But this phase ought not to last very long. Possibly only a year or so. When your child is going through it, if he does, provide him with things that can be destroyed rather than keep curbing this inclination by saying " No " all the time. Offer him some paper that he can tear up into pieces. Provide a piece of wood and a little mallet and let him hit on that. Give toys that can be pulled apart such as a peg board with holes and pegs. Encourage him to make sand pies so that he can bash them down as quickly as he turns them out, and be sure that the home atmosphere is a happy one and that you are not being over strict in his upbringing in general.

Obedience

Obedience is a thing that you must, at certain times, enforce for your child's own safety. Playing with fire is one of those times. Dashing across the road instead of staying by your side is another, and you will have to be quite firm here with both of these. But at times, when obedience is not essential, it is a mistake to insist upon it for its own sake. It is much better to train your baby to do as you say because you have good reason for saying it, and also because it is what he is expected to do.

At the same time you must remember always to give plenty of notice when something has or has not to be done. When it is time for bed, for instance, don't suddenly announce it in the middle of his play and expect him to leave off then and there and start undressing. Say, " In ten minutes it will be bedtime and in five minutes you must start to put your toys away." Then repeat the warning once or twice, if necessary, adjusting the time limit accordingly.

Giving Up Napkins

When daytime napkins are given up it would be far too much to expect no accidents at all. These are bound to occur, so it is better to bear this in mind and be prepared for them. They are generally due to the inaccurate timing of messages running to and from baby's brain. There is the natural desire felt by the body which first has to be registered as a message in the brain. This then has to be translated into one to be transmitted to the bladder. That takes the form of an order to wait for the chamber. Another message has to flash through the brain to send the child to find his mother and ask for what he wants. Still another one has to go to the bladder to authorise it to function when the chamber has been found and put in place.

The first message is usually recorded in due order, but before the other ones can all be completed in their proper sequences, the " accident " has occurred. This explains why very young children so often say what they want immediately after, instead of before, the bladder has been emptied. On such occasions as these you will find it far better to reassure your baby that he will soon learn to ask first and then wait, than to scold him or even reprove him for his mistakes.

Never allow your child to dash across the road.

Over-tiredness, insufficient bed covering causing chilling to the body, getting out of a hot evening bath into a cold bed at night, scolding, unhappiness, anxiety, the presence of worms and the need for more mothering all make it harder for a child to learn to be dry at night.

Some authorities insist that it is important to rouse a child at about 10 p.m. to pass water and make sure that he is sufficiently awake to realise fully what is happening. Others are against this. I have known cases where children have been systematically woken. I have known others where there has been no 10 p.m. lifting at all.

If, after the 10 p.m. bottle has been given up, your baby more often than not keeps dry until four or five o'clock in the morning, as many do, he can be left. If he is constantly wet when you go to bed then he should be roused a little before that time, allowed to pass water, given a clean napkin and tucked up again. Children vary as to how long this nightly lifting may be necessary. Some may require it for a further two or three years; others not so long.

If he should have a wet bed, tell your child you realise it was an accident and that before long he will be able to keep quite dry.

Thumb Sucking

Most babies suck their thumbs or their fingers, particularly when they are tired, bored, unhappy or in need of solace and comfort. More active occupation is needed for baby's hands and mind when thumb sucking takes place in the daytime. At night, when he is in bed, the thumb should be gently taken out of his mouth after he has fallen asleep. Apart from removing the thumb when it is easy to do so, it is better not to draw attention to the habit. On no account should drastic measures be used.

Head Banging

Head banging is in the same class as thumb sucking

but it is not nearly so common. More mothering during the daytime and more of an outward display of affection generally does a lot to reassure the child and provide the added sense of security and comfort he needs.

Temper

You are bound to meet with shows of temper from your baby. Sometimes they may seem very violent to you. Round about the age of fifteen months, kicking and screaming when he cannot have or do just what he wants is very common, but these outbursts of rage are perfectly normal to development and they are nothing to worry about in the ordinary way. Usually the best course at this age is to divert the child's attention. Later on when loss of temper is shown, a wise mother has to make it clear by gentle methods that such displays fail to lead her child anywhere.

The best thing to do then is to ignore the little one while he is angry, so that he comes to understand that only when he is reasonable and behaving properly can he expect to gain his mother's attention. If this does not have the desired effect, sitting him on a chair can be very sobering. If he kicks, remove his shoes.

On rare occasions, it may be necessary to put him by himself in the next room, but if you do this, make sure that he can come to no harm on his own, and be careful to leave the doors open, otherwise you may make matters worse by adding fear as well as temper to his troubles. To a small child, sitting alone on a chair for even one minute can seem like an hour. So never over-do punishments, and the moment he relents be ready with a kiss and a hug, and then look upon the matter as closed.

Masturbation

There are probably very few little children (both boys and girls) who do not play with their private parts at one time or another. If you notice your baby stroking

himself or rubbing the thighs together there is no need
to become worried or alarmed. No harm can come from
this and no injury will be done so long as you treat it in
the sensible, modern way. To take away his hand or
otherwise draw attention to it makes a child feel guilty
about what he has been doing, and the guilt set up can be
injurious and very worrying.

When masturbation occurs very frequently it may be
a sign that baby needs more fun and affection in his
life, or that he gets bored and wants more to do, or that
he is unhappy or troubled. Never scold him for it, or
slap him and never threaten. Let him take one or two
toys to bed. Give him books to chalk and colour, fill
his day with happiness and laughter and things will take
their normal course.

Self-reliance

Children thrive on a certain amount of responsibility.
It helps them to develop self-reliance and self-esteem.
There are many ways that you can foster this in early
childhood. Carrying something of yours for you when
you are out walking is one. Putting your letters into
the letter-box is another. Both are well within the
realms of the two to four years old. Running room to
room errands or going into shops and making a small
purchase while you wait outside are good for a boy or girl
of four or five years old, and are tasks which they often do
very well indeed.

Money

From quite a young age it will be good for your child
to have a little weekly pocket money. This need not
be much. Anything from a penny to sixpence, according
to what you can afford, will be quite enough, but the
important thing to remember is that he should learn to
spend some of it and save the rest. It is a mistake to
insist that it all goes into his money-box. Money has a

Be ready with a kiss.

definite value. It is meant to be spent wisely and a child must learn this little by little. He must also learn that if he spends thoughtlessly his money will not go far. He must be taught, too, to save up for anything he wants badly. When he has enough let him go along and buy it. Encourage him to think of others also, and not always to be getting things for himself. Make a point of his giving one or two pennies fairly regularly to charity or other deserving cause, but let it be one he can understand and connected with children if possible.

Honesty

Complete honesty both to others and to himself is another aspect of character to foster in your child. Try and do this always from a positive angle, not a negative one. For instance, when he wants to take something that belongs to someone else, explain that it is not right to touch other people's belongings, and that kind of thing is just not done. Don't tell him that he is wicked. He is not. At first a baby does not fully comprehend the difference between what belongs to him and what belongs to others. He has to learn.

Shyness

Nearly all children go through phases of shyness but they outgrow them, especially if they are treated with tact and consideration. It is best to leave them to their own devices and not try to get them out of it by suggesting that they have " lost their tongues." If baby is shy with strangers, never mind. Just ignore it and after he has been told to greet them politely, let him run away and play, or sit on your knee, but be careful not to draw his attention to his timidity or to let other people do so either. It makes him feel uncomfortable and conspicuous.

Teasing and Fighting

Where there is more than one child in the family there

is sure to be a certain amount of teasing and fighting Sometimes there is a great deal of it. Much depends upon the ages and sexes of the children. It is not always wise to interfere too much. Little ones have to learn to give and take and to settle quite a number of their own squabbles.

All the same there are times when mother must intervene. The quickest way of settling trouble is to change the subject and suggest some different form of games.

It is very important not to take sides or to show any form of favouritism, but sometimes the smaller of the children (quite often a younger sister) has to be shielded from the fighting of the older one (not infrequently a school-boy brother). But, before rebuking him, make sure that he was not being subjected to quite a lot of teasing. It is not often that all the blame lies with one child, remember. It is generally half and half.

Learning

There is no need to try and hold your child back if he seems quick at learning. Where it comes easily and naturally you can safely let it go along at its own pace, just giving help as and when he asks for it.

On the other hand, you should not force a child to learn. For one thing, you may be teaching him in the wrong way, and for another you may be over-taxing his mental powers. But there is no harm in assisting him when he is trying to master things on his own. Indeed, if you do not, it may cause a clever child to feel frustrated and annoyed. One thing is important, though. If you yourself really do not know the answers to his questions, it is better to admit it rather than to bluff it out, or give the wrong ones.

The Facts of Life

Sex instruction should begin in the home, and when your child starts asking you where he came from, you will know that the time has arrived for you to enlighten him in a few simple but truthful words.

There is no need to go into detail at first. Just try to match your replies to his questions, answering as much as he asks, and no more. His first question may be: " Mummy, where did I come from ? " If it is, you can reply, " You grew inside me." Sometimes, though, a child first asks: " Where do babies come from ? " The answer is very simple: " They grow inside their Mothers."

If you give the information openly and simply, without hesitation and without emotion, you will find that your child will accept it all quite naturally and for a time he will cease to show any further interest in the subject.

A little later on, though—it may be weeks, it may be months—he will broach the topic again : " How was I born ? " or else : " What does ' born ' mean ? " he will want to know. This calls for a longer answer, but even so it should be quite truthful. " You grew inside Mummy, and you kept warm in her womb until you were big enough to come out through an opening that girls and Mummies have in front " is, perhaps, the best way of replying.

It rather depends on his age as to whether this will be sufficient on its own, or whether a further question may be put such as " How did I get there ? " To this you will have to explain : " Everything that is alive has to have a mother and a father. The father puts a little seed inside the mother so that it can join a seed which is already in her. When these two seeds find one another, they join together, and turn into one seed which then grows into a baby." It makes no difference whether it is the mother or the father who gives this information. The parent to whom the question has been put is the one who should give the answer. As a rule, it is the mother, but not always so. Both husband and wife, therefore, should be prepared to enlighten their child when enlightenment is demanded. To be unable to do so or to shirk the responsibility, leads to the obvious conclusion on his part that either his parents are not speaking the truth or else they do not know the facts themselves. As a result he will turn to other channels for information later on, and gain his knowledge from divers sources, as and where he can. This is a very great mistake. It is from you that it should come.

Although in good time baby's attention will be drawn to nesting birds or a cat with kittens and the reproduction of plant life, a child's first interests are directed towards himself and to children like him. So, always answer his questions from the human aspect rather than with illustrations from nature. If he knows the truth about himself, the facts concerning the lower grades of life will all fall into their right places later on. The pollination of flowers is too complicated for a child's mind to grasp at first, and detail such as this should be left until he asks for the explanation himself. It should not be given as a substitute for human reproduction because the similarity between plant life and human life is totally and absolutely different. Your aim, as a mother, must be to answer your child's questions in a way that he himself can understand.

CHAPTER XIII

BABY'S AILMENTS

HERE, arranged in alphabetical order, you will find many nursery upsets and illnesses. Some are serious, most are not; many you will be able to deal with on your own, but in cases where you are in doubt (and always where it is mentioned) you should call in your doctor.

Adenoids

When there is an over-growth of tissue at the back of the nose, which blocks or partially blocks the airway and causes mouth breathing, a child is said to be suffering from " adenoids." The signs of adenoid trouble are : inability to breathe freely through the nose (in bad cases there may be a complete stoppage as with a bad cold), attacks of earache, discharge from the ears and an inclination to deafness. Breathing through the nose should be encouraged and a doctor should be consulted since early treatment may prevent an operation. A course of cod-liver oil is helpful, and the child should be prevented from catching cold as far as is possible.

Animal Bites

Should a child get bitten by an animal, such as a cat or dog, always wash the wound extra well under the tap or in several changes of warm water. If the bite is deep it is best to let a doctor see it as it may need cauterising. In this case antiseptics should not be applied. Small bites after washing should be dressed as for dirty cuts.

Appendicitis

Although it is not very common for a baby to suffer

from appendicitis, this illness can occur at any age in life. It is always serious, but when the trouble is diagnosed early and an operation performed, if necessary, a quick and complete recovery is nearly always made.

The usual chief signs are sudden persistent pain generally in the region of the navel, which makes the child double up, but sometimes the pain does not seem to be very bad. Sickness is nearly always present and there is a raised temperature, though this may not be very high at first. Some children are constipated with appendicitis, others get diarrhoea.

While waiting for the doctor put the child to bed, and give nothing to eat or drink. On no account give any medicine, aperient or oil. To do so might prove very dangerous.

Bed Wetting

Few children are dry at night before the age of two years ; many not before they are three. After about that age, wet beds, with the exception of very occasional ones, are not normal and the cause of the trouble should be sought for and the remedy found.

It may be that the child is not warm enough in bed at night. It may be that he gets out of a hot bath and goes straight into a cold bed, thereby producing a certain amount of chilling to an extra-sensitive body surface, or it may be that he has been subjected to sudden changes of food, or that his usual diet is not properly balanced. Or, he may be over-tired and in need of more sleep.

On the other hand, the cause may lie deeper. It may be due to unhappiness at home or at school, to nervous upsets, to too strict habit training in babyhood or to faulty habit training after the age of about two years old, or to scoldings for being wet or dirty, or for not using the pot at the appointed times.

The first thing to do is to establish a happy and a

confident attitude of mind. Assure the child that he will soon learn to keep his bed dry and to call you when he needs to pass urine.

Lift him at night before you yourself go to bed, waking him sufficiently to be able to understand and to obey the command quietly given to use the utensil. Then assure him that in all probability he will not need to use it again until he is well awake in the morning. Try to arrange for this nightly lifting to take place at the same hour. In bad cases, though, it is sometimes very helpful if the child empties his bladder about 9 p.m. and then again two hours or so afterwards. See that the bedclothes are light but sufficiently warm, and remember that an extra under-blanket is often worth two on top.

A little praise cheerfully given when a child manages to keep dry is comforting and reassuring. When there is an accident, it is much better not to show concern but to treat the whole matter as a mistake. When a child is really old enough he can be encouraged to help make up the bed next morning so long as this is not regarded as a punishment, but merely as helping you to put right something that went a little wrong.

Here and there bed wetting may be caused by actual bladder trouble itself. Therefore, if despite these suggestions, the condition persists, consult your doctor with regard to having urine tests made for pus and sugar or other abnormalities that might possibly be to blame.

Birthmarks

Birthmarks are never caused by anything an expectant mother sees or does or thinks about. Nor are they the result of intercourse or conception during or near to a period. Many of the fainter types of marks fade during the first year of life. Others generally respond well to modern treatment. Never try and treat a birthmark on your own. Always consult a doctor.

Boils

Boils are really little abscesses in the skin. The modern treatment is to keep the boil clean and cover it with a piece of elastic plaster. Or, use a boil plaster. Never foment a boil and never squeeze it. If you do, you may spread the infection and cause another, and you will certainly make it worse. Where a child is subject to boils, medical treatment is needed.

Breasts

Not infrequently the breasts of a new-born baby swell. They may even contain a little fluid, but on no account should they be squeezed. The best thing to do is to protect them with a little cotton-wool placed under the vest. No further treatment is needed as a rule.

Bronchitis

Bronchitis is not uncommon in early childhood. It can quickly follow a neglected cold, though in some children cutting a tooth is a predisposing cause. It is characterised by a harsh, dry cough, difficult breathing and raised temperature. There may be rapid, laboured respiration and bubbling sounds in the chest. Never treat bronchitis lightly. At the first sign put your child to bed in a well-aired but warm room, and call your doctor in.

Place a screen round the head of the bed to keep off direct draughts and give plenty of fluid. All other treatment will be ordered by the doctor, but until the temperature is normal be prepared to give only milk food.

Bruises

Provided there is no other injury and the skin is unbroken, a small bruise can be bathed with very cold water. Then, using only the lightest touch, very gently massage the part round and round with the fingers and some soft ointment, such as cold cream. If the skin is broken the injury should be treated as for a cut, but the bandage put over a bruise should never be tight. Bad bruises should be seen and treated by a doctor.

Burns and Scalds

The shock caused by burns and scalds is out of all proportion to the size of the injury, and all but the very smallest should have a doctor's immediate attention. In the meantime, prevent germs from reaching the burn by tying a clean handkerchief over your nose and mouth and by covering the injury as quickly as you can with a freshly-laundered towel.

The baby should be wrapped up and kept very warm in blankets and taken at once and with all possible speed to a hospital if this is quicker than calling a doctor to the house. Small drinks of warm water or milk may be given at frequent intervals but large ones may cause sickness. In the rare event of a scald in the mouth or throat send immediately for the doctor. Meanwhile, keep the child very warm and give a little cold water to sip. Small burns are generally treated with one of the up-to-date cream preparations. A doctor will generally give a prescription for this enabling a mother to keep some handy.

Chicken Pox

This complaint is seldom serious. It may start by the child feeling feverish and seedy for about one day, but generally the spots are the first signs of the illness. As a rule, few in number, these come out in little groups over a period of about four days, mostly on the face and trunk, though they can appear anywhere on the body. Each successive batch begin as tiny blisters, turn into little postules and then dry into brown scabs which fall off after a few days.

The child should be isolated, generally for three weeks, or until every scab has fallen, if any remain on the skin after this period. He should be kept in bed if he is at all feverish. The spots are often very irritating. When they are, bathing them with an antiseptic lotion helps to allay this. A child with chicken pox should not be allowed to scratch himself since it may cause permanent scarring wherever a scab has formed.

Colds

Colds are very infectious and pass quickly from one person to another. A child with a cold should be kept away from other little ones as far as possible and taught always to cough and sneeze into a handkerchief to prevent the spread of germs. Such handkerchiefs should not lie about, but should be disinfected, washed and boiled frequently. Destructible tissues are better still.

Very young children with bad colds should always be kept in bed. If a hard cough develops call in your doctor as this may be the beginning of bronchitis. Bear in mind that some infectious illnesses start as a bad cold and are generally very contagious during this stage, so if you have any reason to suspect or fear this, or if you know that your child has been in recent contact with someone suffering from an infectious complaint, it is better to isolate him if you can, until you are sure.

Colic

Colic, or wind, is very common in young babies. It may be due to swallowed air which has not been properly brought up after each feed, to prolonged crying, underfeeding, incorrect feeding, chilling, indigestion, dirty bottles, teats and dummies, or to too tight a binder. The treatment consists in finding and remedying the cause. During an attack baby will scream loudly, his face may be puckered and his tightly clenched fists thrust into his mouth. The legs are invariably drawn up to the stomach which, if you touch it, will feel hard.

Passing wind upwards or downwards brings relief, but one attack of colic may be followed quite quickly by

another.   Hold baby up against your shoulder and gently
pat his back.   If wind is not brought up or if he is not
relieved, give one teaspoonful of plain dill water in a
little warm, boiled water, and warm his toes if they are
cold.   In bad cases a hot fomentation applied to the
abdomen is a help, but where none of these simple treat-
ments proves a cure the baby should be seen by a doctor.

Constipation

Constipation is never a disease.   It is due to a bad
habit.   There are several causes, and amongst the most
common are over-feeding, under-feeding, too little fluid
in the diet, muscular inactivity, frequent use of opening
medicines and, in older children, to inattention when
sitting out.   The remedy lies in correcting the diet, giving
extra fluid to drink, encouraging regular sitting-out times
without hurry or fuss, slightly increasing the sugar in the
food, allowing more opportunity for exercise and giving
extra fruit juice or one or two teaspoonfuls of strained
prune juice or the same of prune pulp (stewed prunes
passed through a sieve) according to whether the child is
under or over six months old.

Abdominal massage starting low down on the right
hand side and working clockwise up, across the abdomen
just below the ribs and then down the left side is a help
in bad cases.

Remember that many breast-fed babies only get one
motion every forty-eight hours or even less frequently
still, and that where this is normal when passed (that is
of the colour and consistency of newly-made mustard or
freshly-scrambled egg) it is nothing to worry about.   It
is not constipation.   It is due to the fact that good breast
milk is easily assimilated and contains little waste.

Never give a child strong aperients or enemas and
never insert a suppository or a " soap stick " unless these
have been medically ordered.   The last two especially
are far too irritating and, as a rule, only encourage lazi-
G*

ness without getting to the root of the trouble. More-over, enemas and suppositories may be emotionally upsetting and can be habit forming. Should an aperient really be needed, a little magnesia for an infant, or syrup of figs for an older child, are amongst the most suitable.

Convulsions

A convulsion starts with the child losing colour and with twitchings of the face and limbs. The eyes may roll or they may squint, the neck becomes stiff and the face may go very blue. The body becomes rigid, the head is thrown back and the fists clench during the spasm. Always send for a doctor at once.

In the meantime, if a warm bath is at hand put baby into it and apply a cold compress to the head. Other-wise, wrap the child in a blanket and hold him on your knee, bathing his head with cold water. When the attack is over tuck him up in a warm bed and let him sleep. Never attempt to give anything by mouth to a child in a convulsion or he may choke.

Convulsions are not very common, and if a baby is normally healthy they generally only arise as an onset to some illness or from acute digestive disturbances associated with errors in feeding.

Coughs

Occasional coughs mean nothing as a rule, but frequent coughing, especially if baby has a cold or is teething, should never be neglected. A wise mother will obtain medical advice rather than try and treat a bad cough on her own. If neglected, bad coughs can all too quickly turn to bronchitis in children.

Here is an excellent home-made cough cure which is suitable for slight coughs. It is easily made and com-pletely harmless. Mix together two teaspoonfuls of honey, one quarter of a teaspoonful of glycerine and six tea-spoonfuls each of orange juice and lemon juice. The dose is half to one teaspoonful when necessary.

Croup

The symptoms of croup may be alarming, but the complaint is seldom serious. It is really a sudden attack of breathlessness accompanied by a harsh, metallic cough which generally comes on without warning at night, often in the early hours of the morning. Since diphtheria may begin in this way, a doctor should always be sent for, as early diagnosis in that case is imperative. While waiting for a doctor you can safely apply comfortably hot fomentations to baby's throat, or give him a hot bath. A steam kettle boiling in the room near, but not too near, his cot will help to ease the breathing.

Crumbly Motions

Crumbly motions are uncommon in a breast-fed baby. In a bottle-fed child and in babies on mixed feeding the trouble is due to an unbalanced diet. Probably too much milk is being given, or a preparation containing too much protein. If the milk is diluted by the addition of more water the trouble should vanish.

Crying

All babies cry to a certain extent. A little is natural and healthy. It expands the lungs and provides a certain amount of exercise. Bad crying, though, is different.

When it is due to hunger and thirst, baby's cry is a loud, fretful one ending in a scream of temper. If he is too cold or too hot, uncomfortable or wet, has been lying on one side for too long or has become cramped, he may cry too. So he may if his clothes are too tight, if he is suffering from eczema (owing to the extreme irritation), if he has sore buttocks, indigestion or wind, or earache, and now and again when he is bored. Try to find out what is wrong, but remember that, more often than not, bad crying means baby is hungry.

Curds

Curds in the motions generally mean there is a surplus of one of the ingredients in the milk over and above baby's needs. There is no need to be unduly worried by occasional curds. Persistent white curds, though, in yellow motions point to over-feeding. White curds in green motions are found in digestive upsets and in certain cases of under-feeding.

Cuts

Small cuts should be well washed in slightly salted water, dabbed dry and covered with a ready-for-use dressing. If the cut is a dirty one, wash it until it is perfectly clean, dry it and apply some acriflavine lotion (strength 1 in 1,000) on sterilised gauze. Cover this with cotton-wool and bandage securely but not too tightly. In dressing a cut, always try and draw the two edges together. When the dressing has to be removed and it is difficult to get off, moisten it with some weak peroxide of hydrogen and it should then come away easily. Bad cuts need a doctor's attention, and so do those where there is a lot of bleeding, or where the bleeding keeps coming through the bandage.

Diarrhoea

Never regard diarrhoea lightly. If the trouble is bad, or the child appears ill, or if the motion passed has an offensive odour, a doctor should be summoned immediately. Neglected diarrhoea can rapidly become very serious, especially in hot weather.

Simple diarrhoea is usually caused by errors in diet or feeding, by over-feeding, teething, upsets, chills and indigestion. It can also be due to emotional upset on the part of the breast-feeding mother, or to taking strong aperients herself or giving them to her baby. A warm flannel round the abdomen and attention to the baby's feeding generally corrects a mild attack of diarrhoea.

Or you may be ordered to give a teaspoonful of fluid magnesia and plain boiled water only to drink until the medicine has acted.

In all cases of diarrhoea wash your hands frequently with a germicidal soap, particularly after attending to baby or anything he has soiled.   Napkins, on being taken off, should be placed immediately in a covered pail containing some disinfectant and left there for six hours. They should then be very carefully washed, well boiled and if possible dried out of doors.

Diphtheria

This is always an extremely serious and highly infectious illness, particularly fatal in young children and babies.   The complaint begins with feverishness and general appearance of illness.   Usually a greyish-white patch covers one side of the throat, which may ache and may or may not be sore, but this patch is not always easy to see.   Later, there is enlargement of the glands in the neck and difficulty in swallowing.   There is no rash.

Since a child's life depends upon prompt and early treatment, you should call in a doctor immediately if diphtheria is even suspected.

If more mothers had their little ones immunised against the complaint, it could practically be stamped out in this country.

Immunisation consists of injecting a minute amount of fluid into the baby's arm.   It is perfectly harmless and has no bad after-effects.

While immunisation affords the greatest possible protection against diphtheria, it does not, of course, guarantee that every child so treated will be unable to catch the complaint.   But it is true to say that the very few who, unfortunately do, should only have a very mild attack and no complications.

Discharges

Discharges from any part of a baby's body—eyes, ears, nose, penis, vagina or navel—should never be neglected and home treatment should not be attempted. Always take the child to see a doctor at once, otherwise there may be risk of permanent injury.

Earache

Sometimes a baby gets attacks of earache when he is teething, or if he is subject to frequent bad colds or to tonsil or adenoid troubles. This may be indicated by his putting his hand to his ear constantly and whimpering at the same time. Persistent crying when accompanied by head rolling, feverishness and loss of appetite with tenderness round the ear may be very serious if neglected. If you suspect earache, or see any discharge from baby's ear, a doctor should always be consulted.

Eczema

There may be a hereditary tendency to this complaint or it may be due to unsuitable food, teething, over-feeding, digestive troubles and bowel upsets. It generally starts as a roughening of the skin accompanied by redness. Later, the surface becomes cracked and damp, and scabs may form.

Eczema usually appears on the face, the neck, behind the ears, or in any folds of the skin. The complaint is nearly always intensely irritating, but a mother should know that eczema is not catching. No soap should be used on the affected parts and baby should be prevented from scratching himself. The treatment must always be in the hands of a doctor.

Falls

All babies tumble down, not only once or twice, but many times, especially at the toddling age. They seldom do harm provided they drop from no more than their

own height and do not receive a bad blow on the head.
Even then, hitting the front part of the head is usually
harmless, but a bad knock on the back of the head may
lead to slight concussion.   If a baby appears sleepy after
a fall he should be allowed to rest quietly and sleep for as
long as he wishes.   In such cases it is wise to call a doctor
in.   Usually, though, after a few tears, a little one is none
the worse for tumbling down or even falling off a chair.

Ears

Occasionally a child will push a small object into the
ear, and anything of this kind needs a doctor's skill to
remove it.   Now and again, though, an insect will creep
into baby's ear when he is playing out of doors.   If this
happens you can lie him down on his side and fill his ear
with a few drops of oil.   The insect will quickly rise to
the top, floating on the oil, where it can easily be removed
with a clean handkerchief or whisp of cotton wool.

Feverish Attacks

Some children are much more prone to feverishness
than others.   In very young ones, excitement, new
surroundings and bad crying may sometimes send the
temperature up for a few hours, but it quickly gets right
again.   A raised temperature at other times generally
indicates the onset of some illness.   A doctor should be
summoned and the child isolated and kept in bed.

Fractures

It is very seldom that a baby breaks one of its bones
except as the result of a really bad accident.   In any
case of suspected fracture, cover the child with blankets
to keep him extra warm and then gently but firmly
bandage the injured limb to the body or, in the case of
the leg, tie both legs together.   If you well pad an
umbrella or a stick with paper, this will make a long
improvised splint which you can fasten by means of wide

bandages from the chest to the ankles. Always send for the doctor, and unless you are forced to do so, do not move the child from where he is. If you do move him, make sure that the injured limb is disturbed as little as possible.

Frequent Motions

In a breast-fed baby this trouble may be due to the mother taking aperients, to over-feeding her child or to giving him sugar-water. In an artificially-fed baby frequent motions are generally due to too much sugar in the food, an unbalanced milk mixture, or both. If the motions are greenish, they may point to under-feeding in both breast and artificially-fed infants. Too much fruit juice may also give a baby frequent bowel actions.

Frothy Motions

Frothy motions usually indicate too much sugar in the nursing mother's diet or in the baby's food or water. When this is not the case it is wise to consult a doctor.

German Measles

Although a mild complaint, German measles is a highly infectious one. The rash generally appears on the second day and fades about the fifth. There is usually some swelling and tenderness of the glands, but this soon subsides. There may be a slight rise of temperature, but usually there is no fever, and little, if any, general disturbance apart from the child feeling out of sorts for a couple of days or so. A doctor should be sent for to make sure of the diagnosis. The patient should be kept warm in one room and isolated generally for a fortnight, after which the room and all clothing should be well disinfected.

Glands

Enlarged glands often accompany tonsil and adenoid

trouble. They also occur during an attack of German measles, mumps, diphtheria and in some weakly and tubercular children. Enlargement of the glands can occur in the neck or other parts of the body. A doctor's opinion should always be obtained.

Green Motions

Every now and again most breast-fed babies have a motion which is green or slightly green. If nothing else is wrong there is no need, as a rule, to worry, but if the next one is green also this may point to wind and colic, to improper feeding, to under-feeding, to too much sugar in the food, to the giving of aperients, or, in severe cases, to an infection of the intestines. If the trouble is bad, or continues for more than twelve hours, or if the child appears seedy, or the motions when passed have a bad odour or appear slimy, call in your doctor.

Grazes

Wash the part completely clean and either leave it exposed to the air to heal or apply a little acriflavine cream. Never use iodine. It stings badly. Bad or very dirty grazes may need a doctor's attention and so will those where pain, inflammation, pus (matter), or heat develop in or around the wound.

Grit in the Eye

This can often be removed from the white of the eye by means of a soft camel-hair brush dipped in weak saline (one teaspoonful of salt to a pint of water). Where this is not successful, put a drop of liquid paraffin in the eye. Prevent the child from rubbing the eye, and take him to a doctor or hospital.

Growing Pains

Some mothers talk vaguely about growing pains. After great muscular activity a child may complain of slight aching in a leg for instance but this should soon pass off. There are rheumatic pains, though, associated with childhood which must never be ignored. A doctor should always be consulted when a child complains of pains in any part of the body.

Heat Spots

These may appear as raised, reddish or whitish spots which look rather like the bite of an insect. On the other hand, they may be smaller, resembling the rash caused by stinging nettles. Heat spots are usually due to over-feeding, particularly of foods such as porridge, sugar and bread. Teething, certain summer fruits and in rare cases fish, eggs or some other article of diet will bring on an attack in certain children. Calamine lotion dabbed on the spots forms a soothing remedy. A pinch of bicarbonate of soda in the drinking water usually helps to ease the trouble also.

Hernia

A hernia or rupture is really a gap in the muscle of the abdominal wall through which a part of the contents of the abdomen bulges. The two most common places for a hernia to appear are near the navel and in the groin. The condition is more common in boys than in girls. Constipation and straining always make a hernia worse; in a few cases they may cause one. Crying, unless very persistent and unusually vigorous, will not cause a hernia, but where one is already present, crying tends to make it worse. A doctor should be consulted. If baby is very young he may pad and strap the part but where this is not effective a small operation is a complete cure. Many cases, though, clear up on their own as baby grows.

Hiccoughs

Hiccoughs is not serious in a baby, but it may induce sickness. It is caused by excitement or by jolting the child too soon after a meal. Gulping down food and feeding too fast will also bring on an attack. A lump of sugar is a simple and effective cure for the toddler.

Impetigo

Impetigo is quite a common skin disease, especially amongst children, and it is very contagious. Little blisters which turn to crusted yellowish sores appear on the face and hands, and are spread to other parts of the skin by scratching and the use of infected handkerchiefs and towels. The treatment should be in the hands of a doctor. Everything that touches an impetigo sore must be regarded as contagious. A child suffering from this complaint must have his own toilet articles, towels, clothes, bed and bed linen kept entirely separate.

Indigestion

Indigestion sometimes shows itself by a child waking and crying in the night. The treatment here lies in studying and correcting the diet. Sometimes indigestion may account for bilious attacks and bouts of sickness. When this is so, it may point to a difficulty in the digestion of fats. The cure consists of reducing the fatty foods for a few days, and giving a plainer diet, with extra water, sugared water or well-sweetened fruit juices. When the child has quite recovered, you can begin to re-introduce fat into his diet.

Insect Stings

Children should be taught not to touch or tease insects which are liable to sting. Since a bee leaves its sting behind in the wound, remove this from the flesh before you apply any remedy. Then dab the wound with a spot of alcohol, surgical spirit or some bicarbonate of soda and water. Wasp stings can be dabbed with calamine lotion.

Infantile Paralysis

This is not a common complaint but occasionally

serious epidemics occur.   Infection probably takes place
by the nose or throat and it is more usual between the
ages of two and five years than earlier.   The first symptoms generally are a slightly raised temperature, headache, occasional sickness and alternately drowsiness and
irritability with pain and stiffness in the neck and spine.
The paralysis follows soon after.   Sometimes there are
no warning symptoms, the paralysis being the first sign
that anything is wrong.   The number of children seriously or permanently crippled is small, but proper medical
and nursing care from the earliest stages is very important.   Vaccination against this illness, though, can
now be given.

Jaundice

In a new-born baby symptoms of jaundice sometimes
appear as a yellow tinge to the skin and the whites of the
eyes.   If the child is kept warm, the condition usually
clears up of its own accord without further treatment.
In an older child, jaundice can be serious and a doctor
should be sent for at once if it is noticed.

Knock-knees

This trouble generally indicates a faulty posture but
now and again it can point to a tendency to rickets.
Medical advice should be sought.   Special exercises, cod-
liver oil and plenty of fresh air are always helpful.   In
bad cases possibly a course of artificial sunlight and
additional calcium to be taken by mouth may be ordered.

Measles

Measles starts like a bad, feverish cold and cough.
As a rule the eyes water, there is considerable running
of the nose and the face generally looks puffy.   On the
fourth day small, dark-red spots appear first on the
forehead, cheeks and round the mouth.   Later, the rash
spreads to the whole body.   A doctor should be sent for
at once.   Since measles is highly infectious, especially in

the early stages, the child should be isolated from the very first symptom and kept in bed, screened from a strong light. Allow plenty of fresh air, and see that the room is well ventilated, yet warm. Milk diet may be ordered while there is any temperature.

Mouth Breathing

When a child habitually breathes through his mouth this may be an indication of enlarged tonsils or an overgrowth of adenoids. Or, it may be due to catarrh of the air passages in the nose. In cases where mouth-breathing persists or appears to be getting worse, the child should always see a doctor.

Mumps

Mumps is usually much more painful than serious. It is highly infectious and because complications may follow in some cases, a doctor should always be sent for. The illness starts with a rise of temperature and pain and swelling in the region below the ear. This increases until it involves the whole of one side of the face and one side of the neck. If there is much pain, hot fomentations to the affected parts seem to bring most relief.

There is great difficulty in biting and swallowing, but if the throat and jaws are kept at rest it will help to lessen the pain. For this reason, fluid diet only should be given at first. The child should remain in bed until the temperature has been normal for two days. Isolation should be for a full week after all traces of swelling have disappeared.

Napkin Rash

There are several causes of napkin rash. Amongst the most common are strong urine, diarrhoea, insufficient changing of the napkins, need for more thorough washing of baby's buttocks and surrounding skin at each changing, the use of strong soap or soda when washing napkins, insufficient rinsing, not boiling up the napkins sufficiently frequently after washing and using a napkin a second time after drying it but without first washing it.

In addition, allowing a baby to lie for long in a napkin which has been soiled is very irritating to the skin because when the child passes urine, a chemical reaction is set up in the faecal matter present which quickly reddens the child's flesh and may even cause blistering and soreness.

Careful attention to the washing and drying of baby's buttocks at each changing is the first essential. Smear into his skin a barrier type of baby cream or a little calamine or zinc ointment to serve as a protection and let baby lie napkinless for short intervals now and again to expose the area to the air and light. True napkin rash confines itself to those parts covered in the ordinary way by the napkin.

Navel

Sometimes a baby's navel is inclined to protrude. As a rule this can be corrected quite easily by strapping it with adhesive plaster. You should let your doctor show you how to put this on the first time, but after that you can renew it yourself when necessary. Soreness of the navel of any kind is not a thing to treat on your own. Your doctor should see the part at once, since if it is neglected it can become very serious.

Nose Bleeding

Nose bleeding is often frightening to a child, so while you apply a cold water compress to the bridge of the nose, and firm pressure over the bleeding side of the nose, be sure to reassure him. Treat the trouble in a sitting position, if he is old enough. In case of frequent nose bleeds a doctor should be consulted to determine the cause.

Objects in the Nose
Should a child push anything up his nose close the
other nostril with light pressure and instruct him to
blow hard.   If this is not successful or if he is too young
for this simple treatment take him to a doctor.

Objects Swallowed
If small and round, these generally pass out with the
motions without causing trouble, but a look-out should
be kept for them.   Large, pointed objects that have been
swallowed need a doctor's immediate attention.   On no
account give any medicine or attempt to make the child
sick.   It is not often that a child will swallow anything
of a sharp nature, such as a piece of glass, but if a
doctor has reason to think he may have done, a few
spoonfuls of very stiff porridge or else a cotton-wool
sandwich may be ordered medically.   If so, to make such
a sandwich a thin layer of cotton-wool is put between two
pieces of bread and butter in the hope that the swallowed
object will embed itself in this and pass out of the body
without doing any harm.

Over-feeding
We generally say it is difficult to over-feed a breast-fed
baby, because when he has taken all he needs from the
breast he leaves off sucking.   With a bottle-fed child,
though, over-feeding can occur through giving too strong
a milk mixture by, for instance, using too much milk
powder for the requisite amount of water.   Bad over-feeding can upset a baby.   It can cause vomiting, diarrhoea,
constipation, wind, colic, crying, indigestion, excessive
pains, perspiration round the head during sleep, heat
rashes and restless instead of peaceful slumber.

Pain
Pain is a warning symptom that all is not well with
baby and it is never wise to neglect it.   It is not always

easy to discover the cause. If you are not sure, or if you think the pain is the result of something you cannot correct easily yourself, you should call in your doctor.

Wrong feeding, wind and certain aperients set up abdominal pain. Teething sometimes causes pain in the gums and jaws. These you can deal with yourself by adjusting the feeds or correcting the diet, by seeing that baby brings up his wind, by giving slightly larger quantities of fruit juice, so as to avoid the need for aperients, and by very gently massaging the gums on the outside of the face if baby is teething. Bad pain anywhere or pain in the ears, throat, head, chest, limbs, back or abdomen due to causes other than these just mentioned needs a doctor's opinion.

Pale Motions

Where pale-coloured motions are large in amount and greasy in character they point to too much fat in the baby's diet. Where they are small, formed and constipated they indicate an excess of protein, that is too much meat, fish, eggs, oatmeal, etcetera. Large whitish, pasty motions are found in bottle-fed babies having too strong a bottle mixture. Pale, clay-like motions are generally due to a deficiency in natural bile, and if in addition the child is jaundiced it may mean that there is some interference with the flow of the natural bile. Both these last cases are ones for a doctor.

Pneumonia

Pneumonia is a very serious illness at all times, and particularly among babies and young children, where it can be very fatal. But, provided a doctor is called in in time and new methods of treatment are employed from the onset, the outlook can be quite favourable in these days.

The symptoms of pneumonia are a raised temperature, cough and rapid and difficult breathing, often accom-

panied by short quiet grunts at each expiration. Sometimes the illness starts with a convulsion but not always.
Sometimes sickness is present, generally the face is
flushed and quite often the child may not look as ill as
he is. Some babies with pneumonia have been found
sitting or even standing up in their cots.

Pneumonia in one of its forms may follow a neglected
cold or bronchitis. It can also be one of the complications of measles, whooping cough, influenza and diphtheria.

Poor Appetite

In an apparently healthy child who is of normal or
above normal weight, a poor appetite is generally the
result of over-feeding or of giving snacks between meals.
Slightly smaller feeds or smaller helpings at meal-times
should be given. In other cases the trouble may be due
to general debility, overgrowth of adenoids, inability to
digest fats, emotional upsets, worms, poor health or
rheumatism, and a doctor should be consulted as to which
the cause is and what the treatment should be.

Prolapse of the Anus

This complaint is more readily understood by a mother
as a dropped opening to the back passage. It need not
cause alarm, although many parents become very uneasy
when this happens. The trouble is nearly always due to
strain through constipation or diarrhoea, or to the
presence of thread worms. Occasionally it is caused in
baby boys by difficulty in passing water owing to an
unusually tight foreskin. When the bowel protrudes
wash the part and smear it with grease. Then gently
push it back. The diet should be regulated so as to get
easy motions without straining, and a doctor should be
consulted.

Rashes

Teething upsets and digestive disturbances sometimes
produce a rash of small, bright red, slightly-raised spots

on the face. Occasionally this spreads to the body. This particular rash tends to come out in crops of spots which fade in a few days but may be followed by another crop elsewhere. If the digestion and bowels are regulated and a little calamine lotion applied the rash should disappear. Napkin rash affects the area covered by the napkin (see Napkin Rash). Any other rashes are usually associated with one of the infectious illnesses and a doctor should be called in.

Red Buttocks

The troubles that cause napkin rash can also cause red or sore buttocks. In addition, wiping baby with the napkin that is being taken off also invites this trouble. The treatment is the same as for napkin rash (see page 213), but you can protect the area still further by applying a small square of clean linen to each buttock. Baby should be changed very frequently and kept as dry as possible. The napkins should be frequently boiled and he should never be allowed to lie in a soiled one.

Rickets

Rickets is a deficiency disease. It is caused by lack of sunlight, exercise and vitamins, particularly vitamin D. Rickets is not often seen in these days where mothers pay proper attention to their children's diets, but it used to be quite common. The symptoms are delayed closure (beyond the eighteenth month) of the soft spot on the head, very late teething, bowing of the legs, deformity of the bones of the chest and pelvis, sweating, particularly of the head, and enlargement of the abdomen. The treatment consists of artificial sunlight, an abundance of fresh air, exercise, cod- or halibut-liver oil and possibly courses of calcium and iron tonics. A doctor should be consulted in all cases of suspected rickets.

Ringworm

Ringworm can appear on the body and on the scalp. On the body it forms a dull red, slightly-raised circular patch which is usually covered with fine scales. If untreated, the patch doubles its size within a few days. As it enlarges, it heals in the middle and shows as a red ring with a pale centre. On the scalp, ringworm appears as a scurfy, greyish, bald patch. All ringworm is highly contagious, and a child suffering from it should be kept away from other children. A doctor should be consulted.

Scabies

This complaint is sometimes called the Itch. It is a very contagious rash caused by a microscopic insect which burrows into the outer layer of the skin and causes intense itching wherever it goes. A doctor should be consulted because the complaint can be quickly cured with expert treatment.

Scalds

Scalds should be treated exactly as for burns. Except for the smallest possible scald, the child should be seen by a doctor immediately or taken with all speed to a hospital, well wrapped in a blanket. Great care should be taken to protect the injury with freshly laundered linen to prevent the entry of germs. (See Burns).

Scarlet Fever

This highly infectious illness commences on the first day with a red and sore throat, headache, vomiting, rapid rise of temperature and possibly diarrhoea. The rash usually comes out on the second day and spreads all over the body, with the exception of just round the mouth where the skin remains very white. A doctor should be sent for at once, and the child kept strictly isolated until he is proclaimed free from infection. Children with scarlet fever are usually sent to a fever hospital where they can have specialised nursing attention which might not be possible at home.

Scratches

Wash the scratched part with soap and water and paint with a little acriflavine. Allow this to dry and then cover the scratch with a ready-for-use dressing in order to keep it clean. (1–1,000 acriflavine is the strength to buy.)

Scurf

Quite the best way to treat scurf is to apply a little one per cent thymol in liquid paraffin to the scalp at night, and to well wash the head the next morning. This can be repeated for three nights running and then at intervals. Any chemist should be able to make up this preparation for you quite cheaply.

Septic Spot or Gathering

Where an injury looks red or inflamed, or where there is throbbing or tenderness, the doctor may order a fomentation. To apply this, cut a piece of lint considerably larger than the part to be treated and fold it double with the smooth, not the fluffy side, outside. Lay it in a lengthways-folded teacloth and boil it in a saucepan for five minutes. Hold the ends of the teacloth up to keep them well out of the water. Then, twisting the two ends in opposite directions, wring it out as dry as possible, unwrap and remove the steaming lint. Give it one shake and apply it while comfortably hot. Cover the hot lint with a slightly larger piece of oiled silk, and then with cotton-wool. Bandage over this and renew the fomentation every three or four hours.

Sickness

Where sickness is slight and occurs shortly after a feed, it is not serious in itself. It is caused by baby taking too much or too fast, or failing to bring up wind, or to the food being rather too rich. Severe sickness occurring after feeds, especially if accompanied by loss of weight or poor gains, may be due to unsuitable food (if baby is bottle-fed) or to an inefficient action of the opening leading from the stomach to the intestines.

This last condition is not very common but it can occur in both bottle-fed and breast-fed infants, and since it can be very serious if it is neglected a doctor should be consulted at once. Sometimes an operation is the only means of curing the trouble and saving the child from death through slow starvation.

Sudden attacks of sickness accompanied by diarrhoea or fever are always serious and a doctor should be called immediately.

Sleeplessness
Under-feeding, inadequate bed clothing, too much excitement just before bedtime, over-tiredness and a lack of iron in the diet all tend to cause sleeplessness in a baby.

Sore Buttocks
Sore buttocks result from strong urine, diarrhoea, too much fat in the diet, insufficient changing, the use of soda or too strong soap when washing napkins, under-feeding when this causes frequent small green stools which are very irritating to the skin, or to wiping baby with the napkin (instead of cleansing the parts with soap and water at each change), and to allowing him to lie in napkins which have been both soiled and wetted at the same time.

To cure the trouble use a little oil or grease instead of soap and water when changing baby for a few days, and cover the sore parts with calamine or zinc ointment spread thinly on two pieces of soft linen and applied one to each buttock. Then put on the napkin in the ordinary way and keep baby extra well-changed. To hasten healing you can expose the buttocks to the air and light during the day, powdering them lightly beforehand.

Sore Throat

A sore throat may be due to a cold. On the other hand, it may be the commencement of an infectious illness such as scarlet fever, measles, or diphtheria. A child with a sore throat should be kept away from others, and if he seems seedy or if there is any rise of temperature or appearance of a rash, a doctor should be sent for at once.

Squint

This condition should never be neglected. If your child develops a squint, take him to your doctor or to see an eye specialist, so that proper treatment may be obtained to cure the trouble before it gets bad. A neglected squint can in severe cases cause loss of sight in the squinting eye which grows lazy. Then the sound eye takes over the work of both. Prompt treatment will prevent this and make the lazy eye do its full share.

Strong Urine

Quite often strong urine smelling of ammonia is a temporary condition connected with teething. It may be present for a week or so and then disappear. It also occurs when urine remains for long in contact with a motion from the bowels or when the napkins have not been subject to sufficient boiling. It is not often that it points to too much fat in the diet, or to the child being unable to digest the ordinary amount of fat, but where a mother thinks it may, it is better to have the child's diet properly adjusted by a doctor.

Styes

As a rule the trouble is due to a run-down condition

in the general health and a course of cod-liver oil with malt and iron is helpful. The eye-lash immediately under the stye should be pulled out and the part bathed with hot, previously boiled water. Should the trouble return, and always where a child is subject to styes, a doctor or an eye specialist should be consulted.

Sunburn

Some children are very subject to sunburn, especially fair-skinned, red-headed ones. If the skin is red over only a small area, calamine lotion applied frequently is very cooling and soothing. Over this you can put a light bandage. Where the skin is badly reddened, though, or if there is any blistering, a doctor should be consulted. It is never wise to treat bad sunburn on your own.

Sweating

Many babies sweat a little when they are asleep. It is sometimes a sign of over-feeding or too many bed-clothes. Should the perspiration be profuse, though, it may be caused by poor health or by rickets, and in these cases a doctor should be consulted.

Teething

Providing he has been correctly fed, teething should not upset a child more than to cause temporary fretful-ness and in some cases a smell of ammonia about the urine and the napkins. A little extra mothering goes far towards helping baby over teething time. Frequent sips of cool boiled water, too, give relief in most cases, but where the gums are extra tender, sips of comfortably hot water and also a warm bath are often of more help.

If baby appears to be rather hot and feverish and disinclined for food for a day or so, this should not be pressed. Provided plenty of water is taken, the child soon feels himself again and is happy once more. A small dose of fluid magnesia is useful occasionally, but apart from this baby should need no other medicine. Teething rings or teething beads should be kept well within his reach, because the more biting exercise his gums have the better. It is a mistake to force him to take hard rusks and crusts when they obviously hurt him—as they often do—when a tooth is actually erupting. As soon as it is through and the slight swelling of the gums has subsided he will take to them again.

Thrush

Thrush appears as raised, whitish patches which are about twice the size of an ordinary pin's head on the tongue, inside the mouth, on the palate and inner surface of the cheeks. Thrush patches have the appearance of curdled milk but, unlike milk curds, they cannot be wiped off. A baby with thrush is generally disinclined for food owing to the pain caused by the sucking. Diarrhoea and vomiting are often, but not always, present.

A doctor should be consulted, and after each feed the child's mouth should be very gently swabbed out with some warm boiled water or any remedy prescribed. Small pieces of thin, perfectly clean cotton-wool wrapped round and tied securely to an orange stick make a suitable swab for this purpose. Thrush is seldom seen in healthy babies whose mothers are scrupulously careful to keep all feeding utensils spotlessly clean, and who wash their breasts and nipples before and after each feed.

Tonsil Trouble

The tonsils are situated one on each side of the throat. They consist of lymphoid tissue and it is their function to defend the body against the entrance of germs. Sometimes the tonsils are not healthy, or they become enlarged. Then they fail in their duty and instead of being a help they are a danger rather than a defence.

Symptoms of tonsil trouble are persistent colds or sore throats (or both), poor appetite, coated tongue and tainted breath. The voice may sound thick and woolly and there may be enlargement of the glands of the neck. Generally the health is poor. Sometimes an overgrowth of adenoid tissue accompanies enlarged tonsils, but this is not always the case. A child showing any of the above symptoms should be seen by a doctor who will advise the correct treatment. An operation is not always necessary, particularly when the trouble is taken in time, but when it is required, the improvement in health is often very marked indeed within a very short time.

Unconsciousness

Babies and young children seldom suffer from faintness or fainting attacks. Unconsciousness, therefore, is generally the result of an accident or of a convulsion or occasionally of an illness. Where an accident is to blame, an unconscious child should be kept lying down and very warm. Nothing whatever should be given to drink owing to the grave risk of choking. Should the unconsciousness be due to a convulsion (this is recognised by twitching of the face and limbs or rolling of the eyes), the treatment is much the same, except that the head should be bathed with cold water while the child lies warmly wrapped up on his mother's knee or is held by her in a comfortably warm bath. In all cases of unconsciousness no matter what their cause a doctor should be sent for at once. As consciousness returns the child should be kept quiet and warm, and allowed to fall into a natural sleep.

Under-feeding

Under-feeding may be indicated in several ways. The most common are poor gains in weight, crying at night, sucking ravenously at the breast or bottle, constipation or the passing of frequent, small, slimy, green motions

H

(these are often passed during a feed and accompanied by bouts of wind) and in severe cases a wrinkled instead of a firm skin. The remedy is to feed baby more often, increase his time at the breast or give small complementary feeds from a bottle after the breast feeds. Or, if he is already-bottle fed, to feed him more often, give a larger feed, or re-adjust the milk mixture so as to make it stronger. In a few cases it may be necessary to change the artificial food but this is not often called for.

Whooping Cough

Whooping cough begins very like a cold with sneezing, slight fever and cough. The cough, generally more troublesome at night, gets steadily worse until it comes on in paroxysms (sudden fits of coughing), which often end in sickness. After a week or a fortnight, the characteristic long-drawn-out whoop at the climax of a fit of coughing may appear, but it is possible to have whooping cough and not whoop at all. In older children usually the illness is not serious, but in young ones and also in babies it can be very grave.

A doctor should be sent for and the child isolated, but as a rule he need not be put to bed unless there is any fever. Plenty of fresh air should be provided, the food should be nourishing, and (if sickness is present) should be given in small amounts and after a fit of coughing so that it may remain in the stomach for as long as possible.

During a bad attack of coughing it is a help to the child if the forehead is held and supported. All expectorated and vomited matter should be burnt immediately. The complaint is infectious from the onset—that is, even before the development of the whoop—until two weeks after the cough has disappeared, or if it lingers, for six weeks at least from the commencement of the illness.

Wind

These are the common causes of wind: Under-feeding,

taking the food too fast, over-feeding, too tight a binder, not getting up swallowed air both during a feed and after it, an unsuitable milk mixture (if baby is bottle-fed), errors in feeding, indigestion, cold feet, chilling caused by allowing baby to remain in wet uncomfortable napkins, dirty bottles and teats, and dummies. Try and discover the cause of baby's wind and correct that. Then the trouble should disappear. During an attack, warm the feet, give about two ounces of warm water to which you have added a teaspoonful of dill water, and then hold baby up against your shoulder and gently pat his back. When he has brought up his wind he should be better. In bad cases a hot fomentation applied to the abdomen should bring relief. Wind can usually be prevented by holding him up against your shoulder and gently patting his back, half-way through and again at the end of every feed, and not putting him back into his cot until wind pops have escaped. (See page 132).

Worms

Worms do not always occur in children of poor health. The robust may contract the complaint also. It may cause fretfulness, digestive troubles, bad breath, and itching in the area of the back passage and sometimes a troublesome cough. As there are three types of worms, tape worms, round worms and thread worms, a doctor should be consulted since the treatment for each is different. Of the three, thread worms are the most common.

Until the child is cured, and for some time after as a precautionary measure, wash round the back passage three times daily and after each motion with warm soap and water to which a little mild disinfectant has been added. Then dry and apply a little medicated ointment. The child's hands should be washed frequently and the nails scrubbed. This is particularly necessary before food is taken and should be the unwavering rule at meal-times, since the minute worms' eggs often get lodged round the nails in scratching and are then conveyed to food. Either sew up the bottom of the nightdress or put the child into pyjamas at night and provide gloves for sleeping. These should be boiled daily. Bed and body linen must be changed frequently and well boiled in the wash.

After attending to a child with worms, always wash and scrub your own hands before touching or doing anything else.

One reason why some mothers experience such difficulty in ridding their children of this complaint is that they fail to realise how easily a little one can reinfect himself and also pass the infection on to others.

CHAPTER XIV

SINGLE-HANDED MOTHER

A MOTHER'S life is both busy and interesting—always. This is especially so in these days when she generally has everything to do in the house with very little, if any, outside help.

Sensible Planning

But with careful planning beforehand and certainly a knowledge as to the best way of doing things, she can be very sure of success. Some mothers find it a great help to work to a time-table. Others manage better when they leave each day to map out itself as it goes along.

On the whole, it is a good idea to have some sort of plan, at any rate at first, particularly with the first baby, but the main thing to remember is that it can only serve as a guide. It would be quite impossible and equally undesirable to manage any home and bring up a family too by clockwork routine.

Time-tables

Here are four quite simple time-tables covering the first two years of a child's life. They begin with four-hourly feeding but remember that some babies do better on demand feeding at first. From seven months old onwards, baby's meal-times change from five feeds a day to breakfast, dinner and tea-supper with orange juice first thing in the morning and for a time a bottle feed last thing at night.

1 Week—4 Months Old.

6.00 a.m.   Lift baby. Give him his first feed and after wind has been expelled, wash, dry and powder the buttocks. Put on clean napkins and return baby to his cot for further sleep. Wet napkins are then put to soak.

Return to bed, or rise and dress.

Breakfast and household duties.

9.00 a.m.   Baby's orange juice and cod-liver oil (from one month old onwards).

9.10 a.m.   Prepare and give baby his bath (or morning wash) and his exercises (from two months old).

Hold him out and then dress him.

10.00 a.m.   Feed baby and after wind has been expelled hold him out to pass water and motion.

10.40 a.m.   Baby should sleep out of doors (weather permitting). Household duties, shopping or free time. Dinner.

2.00 p.m.   Bring baby in and feed him. After wind has been brought up, change him. Then put him out of doors for further sleep.

Time for rest, shopping, visiting, gardening or walk. Tea.

4.30 p.m.   Mothering hour. Lift and change baby and allow him to lie on your knee when tiny, or play quietly with you when he is older.

(Orange juice and cod-liver oil can be given at this time, instead of, or as well as in the morning).

5 30 p.m.   Prepare baby for bed. Evening bath, or wash his hands, face and napkin area.

Put on warmed night clothes.

6.00 p.m.   Feed baby. Hold him up to expel the wind. Change him and tuck him up for the first part of the night.

Time for evening meal, sewing or reading.

10.00 p.m.   Lift baby. Hold him out to pass water, if he will. Feed him, hold him up to expel the wind, then hold him out again and finally tuck him up for the night.

It is a good plan to be ready for bed yourself before giving this last feed, as it enables you to get a longer night.

4 to 7 Months Old.

6.00 a.m. Lift baby. Give the first feed and after wind has been brought up, hold him out to pass water.

Return him to his cot for further sleep and put wet napkins to soak.

Return to bed yourself or rise and dress.

Breakfast and household duties.

9.00 a.m. Baby's orange juice and cod-liver oil.

9.10 a.m. Prepare baby's bath, or morning wash.

9.25 a.m. Baby's exercises.

9.30 a.m. Baby's bath.

10.00 a.m. Feed baby and after wind has been expelled hold him out again to pass water and motion.

10.40 a.m. Baby can lie in his pram out of doors (or in his cot in a well-ventilated room in bad weather). He should sleep for two or three hours. As he grows part of this time can be spent in his play-pen—well protected from draughts.

Time for household duties and dinner.

2.00 p.m. Give baby his feed. Hold him out, then allow time for exercise either in his cot, pram or play-pen. He should sleep for an hour at first but as he grows, this gives place to exercise or a walk in his pram.

Shopping, gardening or free time and tea.

4.30 p.m. Baby's orange juice and cod-liver oil.
Mothering hour and quiet playtime.

5.30 p.m. Baby's evening bath or wash.

6.00 p.m. Feed and change baby and after wind has been expelled tuck him up for the first part of the night.

Time for sewing or reading and evening meal.

10.00 p.m. Baby's last feed and change, after you yourself are ready for bed.

7 to 12 Months Old.

7.00 a.m. Rise and dress.

Baby on waking is held out and then given his cod-liver oil and fruit juice.

Household duties.

8.00 a.m. Wash and dress baby. Give him his set exercises.

8.30 a.m.   Baby's and your own breakfast. Then hold him out for motion.

9.00 a.m.   Baby exercises in his play-pen.
Household duties.

10.30 a.m.   Put baby out of doors in his pram for his morning sleep.

Time for household duties.

12.30 p.m.   Fetch baby in, change him and allow playtime till dinner is ready.

1.00 p.m.   Wash baby's hands and face.
Baby's and your own dinner-time.

1.30 p.m.   Change baby and then allow playtime in his play-pen.

Household duties.

2.30 p.m.   Baby goes for a walk with you or is in his pram or play-pen in the garden.
Time for shopping, visiting or gardening.

4.30 p.m.   Baby's and your own tea-time.

5–6 p.m.   Mothering hour.

6.00 p.m.   Baby's bath. Tuck him up for the night.
Evening meal and free time.

10.00 p.m.   Lift baby to pass water. The 10 p.m. feed is generally given up between the age of nine and twelve months.

1 to 2 Years Old.

On Waking   Sit baby out. Then give him his fruit juice and cod-liver oil. Allow him to sit up in his cot (in his dressing-gown) and play until it is time to get up.

Household duties.

8.00 a.m.   Wash and dress baby.

8.30 a.m.   Baby's and your own breakfast. Sit him out for motion. Play until time for morning sleep.

Time for home duties.

10.30 a.m.   Morning sleep out of doors, whenever the weather permits.

Household duties, shopping or out with baby.

12.30 p.m.   Rouse baby. Play till dinner-time.

1.00 p.m.   Wash his hands and face.
Baby's and your own dinner.

1.30 p.m.	Sit baby out and then let him play until you are ready for the afternoon walk.
2.30 p.m.	Afternoon walk or time with baby in the garden.
4.30 p.m.	Baby's and your own tea-time.
5–6 p.m.	Mothering hour.
6.00 p.m.	Baby's bath. Tuck him up for the night.
	Time for evening meal, sewing, reading or amusements.
10.00 p.m.	Lift baby to pass water, if necessary, and finally tuck him up for the night.

Cooking for Baby

You will find it very useful to have some good recipes for baby. When he first starts having solid food many of the ordinary family dishes are not suitable, though they become so as he grows older. Any food you give him should be carefully prepared and always absolutely fresh. The amounts given in these recipes are for this last reason, purposely small.

Home-made Rusks.

Cut some slices of stale bread half an inch thick. Remove the crusts, and then cut each slice into fingers three-quarters of an inch wide. Place them on a baking tin and bake in a very slow oven until they are brown and crisp right through. Store them in an air-tight tin.

Bone and Vegetable Broth.

Wash carefully one large or two or three small bones which have been broken in order to expose the marrow. Place them in a double saucepan (or in an earthenware jar standing in a saucepan of water) and just cover the bones with water. Add a quarter of a teaspoonful of vinegar and simmer for three hours with the lid on. Then add one small sliced potato and an equal amount of two other vegetables according to season, selecting from peas, beans, carrots, lettuce leaves, turnip-top
H*

greens, spinach, beetroot, cauliflower and brussels sprouts. Simmer for one hour more and then strain.

Vegetable Purée.

Select a small handful of tender vegetables. Peas, beans, spinach, beetroots, turnip-top greens, carrots, lettuce leaves and brussels sprouts are among the most suitable. Wash the vegetables well. Boil them rapidly in a very little water, keeping the lid on the saucepan. When just cooked pass all through a fine sieve.

Prune Pulp.

Wash and soak six prunes in water overnight. Next morning stew the prunes in the water in which they have been soaking until they are tender, and the liquid is reduced to practically nothing. Then pass the fruit and what remains of the liquid through a fine sieve.

Cereal Jelly.

Take one tablespoonful of well-cooked porridge and add two tablespoonfuls of boiling water. Well mix and boil for a few minutes. Then strain and set the liquid aside to jell.

To Cook Brains or Sweetbreads.

Well wash the meat and then skin it. Stew it gently in a little milk until it is tender, keeping a cover over the food to prevent it from becoming dry.

Rice or similar Milk Pudding.

Wash a large teaspoonful of rice or similar cereal. Place it in a small dish or saucepan, add a small teacupful of milk and one saltspoonful of sugar. Bake or boil very slowly, until the cereal has absorbed all the milk.

Coddled Egg.

Place a fresh egg in boiling water. Put a cover on the

saucepan and either draw it to one side of the stove or turn off the heat, so that the water no longer boils. Remove the egg in five to eight minutes according to size. The white should be a soft, semi-transparent jelly.

Fish for Baby.

Well wash a small piece of boned, white fish and place it on a plate with a little milk. Cover this with another plate and place over a saucepan of boiling water until it is nicely cooked.

Baked Apple.

Select an apple free from bruises or similar markings, wash and dry but do not pare or core it. Prick the skin in places and bake the apple in a slow oven until it is soft. Then remove the skin and the core and add a little sugar.

Stewed Apple (or Other Fruit).

Add one tablespoonful of sugar to one teacupful of water and boil for five minutes. Then to the boiling syrup add a large apple which has been peeled and cored and cut into slices (or the same bulk of other prepared fruit) and cook very slowly until it is tender.

Oatmeal Porridge.

Soak one ounce of oatmeal in a large cupful of water overnight. Strain the water into a saucepan and when boiling gradually add the oatmeal. Cook for twenty minutes, and then simmer gently until it is done. Stir frequently to prevent porridge from burning.

To cook Liver.

Take a slice of freshly-cut liver and place it in a dish with a very small knob of butter or cooking fat. Cover with greaseproof paper (or a well-fitting lid) and bake in a slow oven till nicely cooked. The liver should be very tender, with the juice running freely. Then pound the meat and juice together, or cut up the meat and serve with the juice according to baby's age.

To cook Rabbit.

Select, cleanse and well wipe one good joint of rabbit. A hind leg is one of the best parts of the rabbit for baby. Place it in a covered saucepan with a little water, and cook slowly until the meat is very tender and comes away easily from the bone. Then, according to age, either pound the meat and liquor, or cut it into very small pieces and pour the liquor over.

To cook Beef and Mutton.

Place the meat in a pan or baking dish in the oven with a knob of cooking fat and bake. Keep the meat well basted and remove it as soon as the outside is cooked. There is no need to buy a separate cut specially for baby, though, when you have a family roast; a small helping from the joint may always be given. His portion should be underdone and either scraped with a knife or cut up according to his age. Serve it with a little of the gravy from the dish.

Baby's Laundry

You will find that just a little extra care when washing your baby's garments will more than treble their life and go a long way towards preventing the woollies from shrinking and the gowns and napkins from losing their colour and soft texture.

Soap flakes are quite the nicest form of soap for all baby's things, and I always advise mothers to buy them in preference to cakes or tablets of soap whenever they can. The flakes can be supplemented by saving scraps of good soap from the household, shredding or grating them finely and then dissolving a cupful of the shreds in an equal amount of boiling water to which you have added half a teaspoonful of borax. When cold, a semi-transparent soap jelly should result which will help to whip up a good lather.

Before studying the best ways to wash the various articles belonging to your child, here are some general rules which, if you follow them, will help to lighten your work and give you really good results.

1. Remove any rings and bracelets which might catch in the material before making a start.

2. Separate the coloured from the white things. Collect all the white clothes *of the same material* and wash the least dirty ones first. After washing all the whites you can use the same water, provided it is not dirty, for the coloured garments.

3. Clothes that have been wetted by baby, and this applies particularly to woollies, should if possible be rinsed out very thoroughly in cold water immediately after use and always before being washed with soap.

4. Use rain water if you can, otherwise add a little borax to the water to make it softer.

5. Rinse every garment in three lots of clear water, or more if every scrap of soap has not disappeared before then.

6. Never soak, never boil, never rub, and never wring knitted woollens. After rinsing them, squeeze out the water without twisting and dry at once. Woollen garments should be washed frequently and not allowed to get so dirty that they have to be rubbed clean.

7. The washing and the rinsing waters should be the same temperature for woolly and flannel garments. Sudden changes from hot to cold water, or vice versa, is very bad for them ; it causes shrinking.

Vests and Knitted Garments.

The water should be about blood heat. Work up a good lather using as little soap as possible, and make sure that every scrap of soap has dissolved. Then wash each garment quickly and separately by squeezing it under the water in the warm suds. Rinse in three lots of water at a similar temperature. Lift out the whole garment at once, gently squeezing all the time, and roll it in a clean towel to remove the surplus water. Lay it flat to dry, gently pulling it into shape as it does so.

Flannel Nightgowns and Petticoats.

Work up a lather as for the knitted garments and dip each nightgown or petticoat into the lukewarm suds. Squeeze and work it about gently under the water. Then rinse in three lots of lukewarm water until all traces of soap have disappeared. Wring, shake out and dry without letting the garments lie about. Iron each one with a moderately hot iron, slightly stretching the cloth lengthwise while you do so.

Cotton Gowns.

Work up a good lather of hot soapy water. Squeeze the clothes in this, rubbing the dirty parts lightly. Rinse in three waters, wring and dry in the open if possible. Iron the gowns while they are still slightly damp. White cotton garments may be boiled, and dried in the sun to bleach them and help to keep the snowy whiteness. Coloured things should be dried in the shade and not boiled unless the dye is guaranteed as fast and to stand boiling.

Silk, Rayon and Nylon Garments.

Wash in a coolish soapy lather, swishing the article about. Do not twist, rub or wring. After thoroughly rinsing, roll each article in a towel to remove the surplus water and spread out to dry in the shade. When nearly dry, iron with a cool iron on the wrong side, first gently pulling the garments into shape.

Nylon should be washed in lukewarm soapy water, rinsed in water of a similar temperature and then rolled tightly in a clean towel. It may then be ironed with a very cool iron. If the iron is too hot it will make a hole in the garment, so always test the iron first on a snipping of nylon kept for that purpose.

Napkins.

Each soiled napkin on being taken off should be rinsed through in cold water immediately, treated with a small stiff brush (kept specially for the purpose) and well rinsed again. It may then be put on one side until it can be laundered. Wet napkins should be rinsed out in cold water before being washed. Use very hot soapy water and thoroughly wash each napkin separately. Wring, open out and immerse several together into boiling suds. Boil for twenty minutes. Then rinse each napkin separately and very thoroughly in three rinsing waters. Napkins should be dried out of doors and in the sun, for preference. When this is not possible, dry them on a line strung high across the kitchen or other warm room. Never dry napkins before a fire as the heat tends to make them hard and rough against baby's tender skin. Muslin napkins can be ironed when they are dry. Turkish towelling ones should be gently shaken out, but not ironed at all.

Blankets and Shawls.

Choose a bright, breezy day for washing blankets and shawls and proceed as for the knitted garments. Blankets should be hung over a line to dry and shaken occasionally; shawls should be pinned out flat to their original size and shape. They are better not shaken.

Drying Hammocks

A drying hammock is a most useful accessory where there is a baby. Slung between the backs of two chairs placed front to front, many little garments can be laid out flat upon it so that the air can circulate freely both above and below them to hasten drying.

You can make an excellent hammock at home very easily from a piece of wide mesh net about three feet long by eighteen inches wide, two rods and some string. Turn in both narrow ends of the net to a depth of one inch to form a hem and stitch them securely. Then thread a rod through each of the hems so formed and attach a length of string to both ends of each of the rods and suspend the hammock between the chair-backs by means of these. When not in use, this hammock is rolled up to occupy very little space.

Removing Stains

However careful a mother may be, her baby's clothes are liable to become marked and stained at times. If the marks are treated at once, and in all cases before washing, they can generally be removed.

Blood Stains.

Soak the stained part in cold water to which salt has been added in the proportion of one heaped tablespoonful of salt to half a pint of water. If this does not remove the stain completely, sponge it with a little peroxide of hydrogen and afterwards rinse with cold water. Never wash a blood-stained article in hot water.

Cod-liver Oil on Woolly Garments.

Place the stained part over a cup and cover it with carbon tetrachloride. Rub it gently with a soft rag, and then wash the garment in the usual way.

Fat and Butter Marks.

Wash the garment in warm, soapy water and the marks should go.

Fruit Stains.

Most fruit stains disappear when the garment is washed if the stained part has been covered immediately with a liberal coating of common salt. Stains which have become dry should be well damped before the salt is used on them.

Grass Stains.

Pour a little methylated spirits on a clean cloth and sponge the part with this until the stain disappears.

Ink Stains.

Pour about a tablespoonful of stale milk into an egg cup. Soak the ink spot in this. Then rinse in cold water and wash in the usual way. Remember that milk acts as a bleaching agent after a time. Coloured garments should not be left in it for too long.

Ironmould.

Ironmould is extremely difficult to remove without the use of highly poisonous chemicals. It is caused by damp clothes coming into contact with iron rust, such as specks of rust on safety pins or the metal ends and buckles of pram straps, or rusty patches on the wash-tub. Dry cleaning will sometimes lessen the mark, and it is worth enquiring about this at any good dyers and cleaners.

Lipstick Smears.

Sponge the material gently with a little carbon tetra-chloride on a soft rag until the mark has gone.

Milk Stains.

Rinse the whole garment in cold water first and then wash as usual. Milk stains should be dealt with the same day if possible, otherwise they soon become very sour smelling and also they may begin to bleach coloured articles after an interval of two or three days.

Scorch Marks.

If these are slight, damp them with warm water and then bleach the part in strong sunlight. If this is not successful, damp a cloth with hydrogen peroxide and lay it over the mark or marks. Cover with a second clean and dry cloth and press with a hot iron. Repeat the process until the scorch has gone. Severe scorch marks cannot be removed, because the material itself will have been too badly damaged.

Tea Stains.

Add a teaspoonful of borax to a cup of warm water and soak the stained part in this. Afterwards wash in the usual way.

Note:—Peroxide of hydrogen, methylated spirits, long immersion in milk and strong sunlight should be used very cautiously on coloured materials. They may effect the shade or even cause bleaching. In these cases it may be better to have the marks removed (or lessened) by professional dry cleaners. If you decide on this course, attempt no treatment on your own. Instead, attach a note to the garment saying what caused the stain, if you know it, and how long it has been there.

Home Nursing

Where there are children, there are bound to be occasional upsets and illnesses which will certainly need your help and may necessitate days in bed. Close to the nursery, or in some handy place in your home, therefore, should be your medicine cupboard, kept under lock and key, with the key put where little fingers cannot reach it. The contents should be quite simple and include the following:—

Aspirin tablets	Glycerine of Thymol
*Bicarbonate of Soda	Hot water bottle (and cover)
Boiled sugar sweets	*Mackintosh sheet
Camphorated Oil	Medicine spoon
Clinical thermometer	*Methylated Spirit
Cotton-wool	Safety pins
Cough Mixture	Syrup of Figs
Feeding cup or mug	Talcum Powder
*Friars Balsam	White surgical lint

For a still simpler list omit the items marked*.

It is essential to have a first aid box too. These can be bought in different sizes already packed with the requisites you may need. Or you can make up your own, putting into it these things:—

Acriflavine (1-1,000 in water)	Eye drops
	Oiled silk
Adhesive plaster	Peroxide of Hydrogen
Bandages in 3 sizes	Pocket torch and scissors
Bicarbonate of Soda	Ready-for-use dressings
Bottle of antiseptic	Safety pins
Calamine Ointment	Sterilised gauze
Camel hairbrush	Surgical spirit
Cotton-wool	White surgical lint

Illnesses

When your child has to remain in bed you must decide where you are going to nurse him. This will depend on your household and what you have to do.

It is often very difficult indeed for a single-handed mother to run the home, and also act as nurse in an upstairs bedroom. Sometimes, of course, this has to be done. But when the little patient can be moved and it is safe for him to do so, to nurse him in a downstairs room will save you many journeys up and down. Although sick children are often extremely easy to manage, very good and very quiet so long as someone is near, they do hate being alone (even for a moment or two) when they are awake.

The Sick Room

While the room in which the sick child is nursed should be well ventilated with the window open a little both top and bottom and a small fire in the grate (except when the weather is very warm), you must be careful to see that the bed is not in a direct draught. Draughts run between the door and the window, the door and the fireplace and the fireplace and the window. They also run along the floor level. The bed or cot, therefore, should be well raised from the floor as well.

Keep medicines under lock and key and out of reach.

Bed and Bedclothes.

The bedclothes should be light and warm. It is a mistake to pile them on especially if the child is hot and feverish. Aim at keeping him comfortable, removing or adding a blanket whenever necessary. Keep the bed free from crumbs and the bottom sheet or blanket free from creases. A small sheet folded in four lengthways and placed across the bed under the hips provides added comfort, because a fresh section can be drawn through at intervals give to your patient a cool and creaseless part to

Fig 41

The safest place to take your baby's temperature is in his groin.

lie on. The pillow, if one is used, should be shaken up and turned frequently. If the child is under the age of eighteen months, only small flat pillows should be used, and they should not be filled with feathers in case the baby turns on his face and is unable to breathe easily.

Taking the Temperature

A sick child's temperature should be taken night and morning and in bad cases at 10 a.m. and 2 p.m. as well. Shake the thermometer down and place it in the fold of the groin after you have wiped the skin free from any

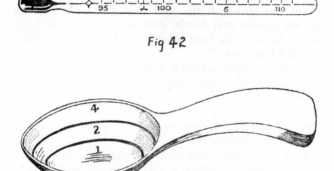

Fig 42

Fiq 43

perspiration. Then bend the leg slightly upwards (Fig. 41) to keep the thermometer firmly in place and leave it there for five minutes. It is never wise to take a young child's temperature in his mouth in case he bites off and swallows the end of the thermometer. Hold it in place in the groin all the time, and after removing it read off and record the temperature on paper or in a note-book kept for the purpose. Then shake the thermometer down, and after washing it in cold water dry it carefully and replace it in its case. The normal body temperature is 98·4 F. and this is marked with a small arrow (Fig. 42).

Remember that some children run a temperature very

easily. At the same time a doctor should always be informed in cases where it remains above normal for more than twelve hours and always should it be over 101° F.

Washing in Bed

The body should be washed all over with hot water and soap every day. It is best to let the child lie between two warmed blankets for this. Dry him with a warm towel and then rub the heels and the buttocks with talcum powder and dust a little on to the folds of the skin. Remove the bath blankets and dress him in fresh warmed bed wear.

The hair should be kept well-brushed. A little eau-de-Cologne will help where there are tangles.

The mouth and lips need special attention. If the child is well enough you can clean his teeth in the usual way. Where this is not easy, glycerine and water may be used for cleaning the tongue and a weak glycerine of thymol mouth-wash and gargle given two or three times a day. Younger children should have their mouths very gently swabbed out with glycerine of thymol diluted with water. A trace of lanoline cream on the lips will help to keep them clean and comfortable.

Medicines

Medicines should be measured in a graduated medicine spoon (Fig. 43) and poured into a feeding mug. They should always be given strictly to time if the child is awake, but unless the doctor orders it never waken a patient to take his medicine, and never repeat a dose if he is sick afterwards but report this to the doctor. If the medicine is unpleasant warn the child of this beforehand and give a sweet or a small piece of chocolate to eat after it.

A cough can often be relieved by sips of cold water, a drink of hot milk, a little honey on a spoon, an additional pillow or a change of position.

Food

An ill child needs plenty of liquid. The more he has the better. Water, lemonade, barley water, fruit juice and water, glucose water (2 tablespoonfuls of glucose to one pint of water), beef tea, clear broth and milk are all suitable, but which you give will, of course, depend upon his age, and the doctor's orders.

It is not easy to drink out of a cup when lying down. If a child is past the feeding-bottle age, drinks can be offered from a spoon, but since this way of taking is rather tedious, except to the small baby, it is better to offer liquid food in a feeding cup, a small jug or let the child drink it through a straw. Put your left hand under his pillow while he is drinking and raise his head and shoulders a little. Be sure to place a napkin under his chin to catch any drips.

Solid food should not be given until the doctor allows it. Then a little very thin bread and butter is generally the best thing for a start, followed by milk puddings, eggs, fish and mashed potatoes in turn. Offer very, very small helpings at first so that the appetite is not over-satisfied.

Never have a scene over food or medicine. If it is flatly refused, just let the doctor know.

Things to Note

You should keep an accurate written account of such details as temperature, bowel actions, sickness, the amount of sleep taken, inclination or otherwise for food, what was given, how much has been eaten and complaints about pains, headache and earache. Any vomited matter should be kept for the doctor's inspection. Wring a cloth out in disinfectant, cover the bowl with this, and then keep it outside or in the lavatory until the doctor has been.

You will find it a help to know the bad signs in illness and also those which show that health is returning.

These are the bad ones : Shivering attacks, profuse perspiration, great restlessness, persistent sighing, tight, rapid or noisy breathing, phlegm which becomes a rusty colour, bleeding of any kind (except slight nose bleeding), bad or abnormally coloured sickness, sharp pains, squinting or a difference in size of the pupils (which was not there before), the sudden appearance of spots and rashes, swellings, difficulty in swallowing, aching in the throat, a sudden rise or a sudden fall of temperature, blueness round the lips and a cold or clammy skin. In all these cases the doctor should be informed at once.

The good signs showing that the child's condition is improving are : Return of the appetite, a better colour, the request for toys or playthings, an increasing interest shown in all that is going on around him, lower temperature and less dozing during the day time.

Getting Up Again

Most children have remarkable powers of recovery and are quickly their lively selves again. When a child starts getting up again after an illness, it is best to allow him out of bed for short intervals to begin with so that he does not get too tired. A tonic is generally ordered during convalescence, and to obtain the best results this should be given with unfailing regularity. A change of air is also good, but where this cannot be arranged try and get him out into the open for long hours at a time.

Keeping Baby Well

Although baby is bound to have his off-days now and again your biggest aim, of course, will be to keep him always well. Towards this end you will find it a great help to attend an Infant Welfare Centre with him at regular weekly or monthly intervals during his early years if you can, so that his progress can be noted by the doctor in charge, and any questions you may want to ask can be answered by someone who has made a special study of the management and the health of children.

At one of these clinics your baby will be weighed carefully, and you will be given advice on hygiene, routine and feeding, all of which will be immensely valuable in assisting you to make yours the really lovely child and the strong and healthy future citizen you would, I know, wish him to be.

INDEX

Join more than 60 million people

who have reached their goals with

Teach Yourself®

and never stop learning.

Launched in 1938, Teach Yourself® has helped over 60 million readers learn the skills they need to thrive in work, study and life. Now, 80 years on, there are Teach Yourself® books on everything from starting a business and learning a language to writing a novel and playing piano.

To find out more about books in the Teach Yourself® series, visit:

teachyourself.com